UNIT 3: EXPRESS YOURSELF

UNIT 2: FIGURE IT OUT

UNIT 3: STARTING NOW

Short Vowels

Circle the word that names each picture.
Then write the word.

1.    frog

   dog

   _____

2.    hand

   leg

   _____

3.    sleep

   bed

   _____

4.    lips

   mile

   _____

5.    star

   sun

   _____

6.    net

   get

   _____

7.    hand

   mitt

   _____

8.    pan

   cook

   _____

9.    bowl

   cup

   _____

10.    sock

    rod

    _____

At Home: Have children think of other words that
have the vowel sounds of the words they selected
above.

1

Vocabulary

Write the word from the box that completes each sentence.

lucky	homework	crawls
shy	carrots	hurry

I. It was eight-thirty. Judy had to _____ to school.

2. Larry does his math _____ every night.

3. The furry rabbit loves to eat _____.

4. My pet lizard _____ through the grass.

5. The new kid on the block sometimes feels _____
   when he makes new friends.

6. Emma felt _____ when she found the gold.

2

At Home: Have children make a drawing of one of the
sentences.

Book 2.1/Unit 1
Ann's First Day   6

Little Rabbit and the Big Hop

"Wait," said Miss Bunnie to Little Rabbit. "Just try it first."

Little Rabbit gave a little hop.

"It was just a small jump," he said.

"But it was a good first try," said Miss Bunnie. "It is hard to hop at the start. But it will get easier as you do your hop homework."

Little Rabbit smiled and hopped all the way home to show his mother.

At Home: Ask the children what was hard for Little Rabbit in this story. Then talk about what might be hard for them in school.

4

"Hurry!" said Little Rabbit's mom.
"You will be late for hop class!"

"But I cannot hop," said Little
Rabbit.

"You will learn," said his mother.

"Can't I stay with you?" he asked.

"Not now," his mother said. "You
need to get to class." She gave him
some carrots for lunch and kissed
him good-bye.

Ann's First Day McGraw-Hill School Division

At hop class, Little Rabbit was
shy. He put his ears over his face
to hide.

"What do rabbits do?" Miss
Bunnie asked the class.

"Hop and jump!" said a tall rabbit.
Then he took a big jump over his desk.

"He is a lucky rabbit," said Little
Rabbit. "I cannot hop like that."

Story Comprehension

Think about the story "Ann's First Day." Answer each question. Use a complete sentence.

1. What did Ann's old class give her? _____

_____

_____

2. What did Robbie do on Ann's first day of school?

_____

3. What did the children do when they saw Robbie?

_____

4. How does Ann feel at the end of the day? Why? _____

_____

_____

4 Book 2.1/Unit 1
Ann's First Day

At Home: Have children tell the story of "Ann's First Day" in their own words.

3

Use Parts of a Book

Study the **title page** and the **table of contents**.

A Winter of Snow	Table of Contents

A Winter of Snow

by Alma Curaqua

Illustrated by
Harold Merton

Table of Contents

1. The First Flurries   2
2. An Ice Storm   7
3. Get Out the Shovels   13
4. Snowbound   26
5. The Big Melt   39

Complete the sentences below.

1. _____ is the title of the book shown above.

2. This book was written by _____.

3. The chapters of this book are shown in the _____

_____.

4. The chapter called _____ can be found on

page 39.

5. There are _____ chapters in this book.

6. The illustrations are by _____.

4

At Home: Ask children to make up another chapter
name that would be appropriate for this book.

Book 2.1/Unit 1
Ann's First Day   6

Short Vowels

Read the sentence. Circle the word that completes the
sentence. Then write the word on the line.

1. The _____ is tan.

pan

cup

plate

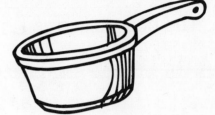

2. The pig has a _____.

hat

wig

cat

3. Jed is in _____.

town

bed

trouble

4. The _____ is on the rug.

boy

car

bug

5. The pot is _____.

cold

hot

mine

5 Book 2.1/Unit 1
   Ann's First Day

At Home: Have children think of a word that rhymes
with each word they circled.

5

Short Vowels

Read the sentence. Circle the word that completes the sentence. Then write the word on the line.

1. The baby is in a _____.

   wish

   tick

   crib

2. I write with a _____.

   pen

   men

   hen

3. Rabbits like to _____.

   pop

   hop

   hot

4. I drink from this _____.

   bun

   cup

   stuck

5. The children are in _____.

   class

   hand

   pat

At Home: Have children identify all the words in this exercise that have the same short **i** sound as in **miss**.

Book 2.1/Unit 1
Ann's First Day

5

Make Predictions

Read the story. Write the answers to the questions.

Alex has a job helping Mr. Jones deliver papers every day. His friend, Jay, would like a job. He wants money to buy his mom a birthday present. Mr. Jones needs only one person to help him. Alex cannot give Jay the money, but he can give him something else for a little while. With a smile, Alex goes to talk to Mr. Jones.

1. What do you think Alex will say to Mr. Jones?

   I think Alex will say to Mr. Jones
   _____

2. What do you know that helps you make your prediction?

   _____

   _____

3. What do you think Jay will do to get some money?

   _____

   _____

4. What do you think Jay will say to Alex?

   _____

   _____

4 Book 2.1/Unit 1
Ann's First Day

At Home: Ask children to use their predictions to make up the ending to the story.

7

Inflectional Endings

The endings of an action word tells if the action is being done by one or more than one individual.

Harry move**s** the box.
Harry and Jim move the box.

Underline the word that completes each sentence. Then write the word.

1. The loud noise _____ the dog.

   scare   scares

2. All the students in the class _____ for the pet bird.

   care   cares

3. The rabbit quickly _____ across the park.

   dash   dashes

4. Rob _____ the name of the new bookstore on

   Green Street.

   knows   know

5. The boys and girls _____ their teacher very much.

   miss   misses

6. The happy rabbit _____ his nose at the class.

   wiggle   wiggles

At Home: Help children to write a three-line story about a new class pet. In the story the children should use verbs that end in **-s** or **-es**.

Long Vowels

Use the words in the box to answer the riddles.

plane	tune	tape	home	time	line

1. I fly high in the sky. What am I?

   _____

2. I am a row of chairs in a classroom. What am I?

   _____

3. Sometimes I seem slow. Sometimes I seem fast. You can tell me with a clock. What am I?

   _____

4. You hear me on the radio. You whistle me. Sometimes you even hum me.

   _____

5. You live in me. I have a front door. What am I?

   _____

6. I will help you stick paper together. What am I?

   _____

6 Book 2.1/Unit 1
   Henry and Mudge

At Home: Help children think of other words with the vowel sounds of the selected words above.

9

Vocabulary

Read the sentences. Choose words from the box that mean almost the same thing as the underlined word or words in the sentences. Write the words from the box on the lines.

worry	hundred	parents
searched	different	weighed

1. Jimmy <u>looked</u> for his truck under the bed.

_____

2. Amy <u>found out the heaviness</u> of the bag of food.

_____

3. I miss my <u>mother and father</u> when I go to camp.

_____

4. These coats are <u>not the same</u> colors.

_____

5. Gloria has more than a <u>large number</u> of baseball cards.

_____

6. My mom will <u>be afraid</u> if we play with her best necklace.

_____

At Home: Have children rewrite the sentences, replacing the underlined words with vocabulary words.

Finding a Friend

The next day Fluffy was gone!

"Don't worry," said Pam's mom, "We have not searched everywhere yet."

Then the doorbell rang. Sue was not alone. She had Fluffy in her arms.

"She came to my home to play with Bud. They are new best friends," she said.

"Let's be friends, too!" said Pam. "Okay!" said Sue.

At Home: Have children discuss how Fluffy and Bud were like each other. How were they different?

4

10a

"You are my only friend now, Fluffy," said Pam. She was sad. Her best friend had moved away two days ago.

Fluffy jumped down and ran toward a giant dog on the street.

"Keep your cat away from my dog," said Sue. Sue was someone Pam had never seen before.

Pam grabbed her cat and went inside.

Henry and Mudge McGraw-Hill School Division

From her parents' room Pam watched the girl and her dog. They should walk on a different street, Pam thought.

On the sidewalk, Sue walked and talked with her dog. "That cat was mean," said Sue. "It must have weighed one hundred pounds! I don't like this new place, Bud."

Story Comprehension

Think about the story "Henry and Mudge." Write the answer to each question. Use a complete sentence.

1. Why did Henry want a dog?

_____

_____

_____

2. How did Mudge change in this story?

_____

_____

3. How did Henry feel about walking to school with Mudge? Why?

_____

_____

_____

4. How would you describe the friendship between Henry and Mudge?

_____

_____

_____

4 Book 2.1/Unit 1
Henry and Mudge

At Home: Ask children to tell what they liked best about this story.

11

Use a Contents Page

Shown below are the **contents pages** of two books about costumes.

| **Halloween Dress-Up** |
| by Ramone Paddington |
| 1. Masks   1 |
| 2. Hats and Scarves   2 3 |
| 3. Dresses and Capes   4 6 |
| 4. Pants and Shorts   7 8 |
| 5. Shoes and Boots   1 0 1 |

| **Costumes for the Theater** |
| by Nora Tishman |
| 1. Cave Men and Women   4 |
| 2. Knights and Maidens   22 |
| 3. Armies and Soldiers   55 |
| 4. Cowboys and Cowgirls   89 |
| 5. Astronauts   129 |

Read the statements below. Then look at the tables of contents to decide which book would best help you. Write that book on the line.

1. You want to find out about bird masks. _____

2. You want to find out about swords for a knight costume.

    _____

3. You want to dress up like an astronaut. _____

    _____

4. You want to find out what kind of shoes a scarecrow might wear.

    _____

5. You want to make a hat with lots of fruit on it.

    _____

At Home: Have children make up a question about each table of contents page.

Book 2.1/Unit 1
Henry and Mudge
5

Long Vowels

Finish each sentence below. Circle the word that completes the sentence. Then write the answer.

1. I went to school on my _____.

   hike   bike   tire

2. The horse's _____ was long and brown.

   mane   tame   cape

3. Pam ate an ice-cream _____.

   bone   rode   cone

4. The _____ baby laughed.

   cute   tube   tune

5. Dad _____ soup for lunch.

   wade   made   cage

6. Mom was wearing a _____.

   code   note   robe

7. Stanley ate all the _____ plums.

   ripe   hike   fire

8. The children saw a _____.

   game   gave   late

At Home: Have children draw a picture of one of the sentences above and then write the words to describe the drawings.

Long *o: o-e;* Short Vowels

Use the words in the box to answer the riddles.

nest	rug	pig	jam	nose	pond

I. You use me to smell things. What am I?

_____

2. Fish swim in me. What am I?

_____

3. I lie on the floor. What am I?

_____

4. People eat me with bread. What am I?

_____

5. Birds live in me. What am I?

_____

6. I am an animal on a farm. What am I?

_____

At Home: Have children start a separate list for each
short vowel sound and put the words from this
exercise on these lists.

Book 2.1/Unit 1
Henry and Mudge
6

Story Elements

Think about the story "Henry and Mudge." Write one or more words to tell what happens to Henry in the story.

Henry is lonely.

↓

1. He asks his parents for a
_____.

↓

2. He asks his parents for a
_____.

↓

3. His parents say
_____.

↓

4. Mudge grows up to be
_____.

↓

5. Mudge and Henry walk to
_____.

↓

Henry is happy.

5 Book 2.1/Unit 1
Henry and Mudge

At Home: Have children tell why Henry is happy.
Have them write a sentence about their answer.

15

Inflectional Endings

The ending of a word can tell you when the action takes place.

Henry patt**ed** the dog this morning.
Henry is patt**ing** the dog now.

barking	petting	rubbed	walked
grabbed	waiting	looking	wanted

Complete each sentence with one of the words from the box.

1. After breakfast Max _____ his backpack from the chair and left for school.

2. The dog is _____ at the cat in the tall tree.

3. The children are still _____ for the school bus at Oak Street.

4. When she woke up in the morning, Julia _____ her sore arm.

5. The children _____ to get a new dog.

6. This morning Anna _____ all the way to school.

7. The lost cat is _____ for his home.

8. Jose is _____ his new puppy.

At Home: Ask children to make up three original sentences about a favorite book or story that uses verbs ending in **-ed** or **-ing**.

16

Book 2.1/Unit 1
Henry and Mudge

8

Long *a* and Long *e*

Write the word from the box that names each picture.

hay	rain	beach	field	tree

1.

_____

2.

_____

3.

_____

4.

_____

5.

_____

5 Book 2.1/Unit 1
Luka's Quilt

At Home: Help children write sentences using the
words they wrote on this page.

17

Vocabulary

Choose a word from the box to answer each question. Write the word on the line.

idea	remember	serious
answered	garden	grandmother

1. Where do roses grow? _____

2. Who is the mother of your mother or your father?

   _____

3. What is another word for a thought? _____

4. What do you do when you think of the past? _____

5. If something isn't funny, what might it be? _____

6. Jill asked Beth a question. What did Beth do? _____

18

At Home: Have children make up riddles for some of the words in the box.

Book 2.1/Unit 1
Luka's Quilt
6

Every Quilt Tells a Story

"I understand," said Tanya. "Even if it is cold, your quilt garden will be safe. That is a good idea!"

"And I will be able to see it, fresh and green, every day!" said her grandmother. "That is my story, Tanya."

"I think I will make a quilt, too," Tanya said. "It will be white and gray, the same colors as your beautiful hair. And it will be filled with animal shapes."

At Home: Help children create a scrapbook or a poster that holds important memories.

4

18a

"What are you doing?" asked Tanya.

"I am going to tell a story," answered her grandmother.

"What will you say?" Tanya asked.

"Wait," answered her grandmother. "You will see me tell the story. I will tell my story with a needle and thread."

"That is a quilt, not a story," said Tanya. "You are making a joke."

"No, I am serious," said her grandmother. "Like a story, a quilt is a way to remember."

"What do you remember?" asked Tanya.

"See this spot with flowers? I will remember my garden when it is cold out. When I sleep underneath it, I will dream of the green leaves."

Story Comprehension

Think about "Luka's Quilt." Put an **X** by each sentence that tells about something you read in the story.

_____ I. Tutu and Luka live in Hawaii.

_____ 2. Luka wants to make Tutu a quilt.

_____ 3. Luka likes colorful flowers.

_____ 4. Tutu tells Luka to choose many colors for her quilt.

_____ 5. Luka is sad when she first sees the quilt that Tutu made for her.

_____ 6. Tutu calls a truce and takes Luka to Lei Day.

_____ 7. Luka decides to make her lei only one color.

_____ 8. Luka and Tutu are still angry with each other after Lei Day.

_____ 9. Luka's lei gives Tutu a colorful idea.

_____ 10. Now Luka likes both her green and white quilt and her quilted lei.

10 Book 2.1/Unit 1
Luka's Quilt

At Home: Ask children to talk about special times they have spent with their grandparents or older friends.

19

Read a Glossary

A **glossary** is like a dictionary at the back of a book.
It gives definitions for words in that book.

---

cheer To give a shout of happiness or encouragement. We all wanted
to *cheer* when Tina ran in the race.
  cheer (CHIHR) *verb*
  cheered, cheering.

chocolate A food used in making sweet things to eat. Billy unwrapped
the bar of *chocolate*.
  choc • o • late (CHAWK liht)
  noun, plural **chocolates**.

Use the sample glossary to help you answer the questions below.

1. Is **chocolate** a noun or a verb? _____

2. How is a glossary arranged? _____

3. What is chocolate used for? _____

4. What word means to give a shout of happiness? _____

5. How many parts does the word **chocolate** have? _____

Long *a* and Long *e*

Write the word from the box that names each picture.

beads	bay	rain	bee	field

1.

_____

2.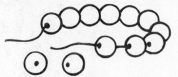

_____

3.

_____

4.

_____

5.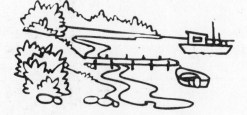

_____

At Home: Help children to write a poem using some
long **a** and long **e** words on this page.

Long *a, e, i, o, u*; Short Vowels

Circle the word to complete the sentence. Then write the word on the line.

1. The dog chews on a _____.

   joke   bone

2. I wear this _____ on my birthday.

   dress   mess

3. A fluffy kitten is very _____.

   brute   cute

4. We drove into town in the _____.

   van   jam

5. The cat _____ under the bed.

   hid   bib

6. Let's go out and play in the _____.

   rain   pail

7. We _____ hay to the horses.

   sheep   feed

8. I serve the food on a _____.

   tray   tail

At Home: Have children choose one of these sentences and write a short story about it.

Story Elements

Characters are the people in a story. The **setting** is where and when the story takes place.

Read the story. Answer the questions.

Fay sat in the back of the class. Outside, the morning sun was peeking out from behind a rain cloud. Fay felt sad. Her dog had just had puppies. She couldn't wait to get home and play with them.

Fay's teacher, Mrs. Johnson, asked Fay why she was sad. Fay told the class about the puppies. Mrs. Johnson told Fay that next week she could bring the puppies in for a visit. Fay was happy about that!

1. Who is the main character? _____

2. Who are the other characters? _____

_____

3. Where is the story set? _____

_____

4. Where does Fay sit? _____

_____

5. When does the story take place? _____

_____

5 | Book 2.1/Unit 1
Luka's Quilt

At Home: Have children write one more sentence using the characters and settings from the story above.

23

Context Clues

Use word clues in the same sentence or in nearby sentences to help guess the meaning of a new word.

Look at the underlined word. Use word clues to guess what the word means. Then draw a line to what the word means.

1. Luka wanted a pretty green quilt.

2. My grandmother used a big needle to baste the pieces of the quilt together.

3. Lee and Jim are planning a trip to Hawaii.

4. Jack loved to smell the fresh blossoms.

5. I wanted to eat bento for lunch today.

6. Because we are friends again, I do not feel angry at you.

7. The big lion roared in his cage.

8. The boy's cap fell off his head.

a. a place

b. a color

c. flowers

d. a hat

e. sew

f. an animal

g. a food

h. mad

At Home: Help the children identify four new words that name or describe objects in their home. Then have them write a sentence that gives a clue to each word's meaning.

Long *i* and Long *o*

Write the word from the box that names each picture.

light	boat	pilot	sky	throw	toe	go	cry

1.  _____

2.  _____

3.  _____

4.  _____

5.  _____

6.  _____

7.  _____

8. 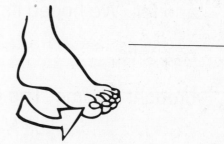 _____

8 Book 2.1/Unit 1
The Roundup at Rio Ranch

At Home: Help children to make flash cards of words that have the sound of long **i** or long **o**.

25

Vocabulary

Read the story. Choose words from the box to complete
the sentences. Write the words on the lines. Then reread
the story to check your answers.

cattle	fence	broken
carefully	gently	safety

Last summer, we stayed at a big ranch. Many

horses and _____ lived there. One

day a calf got away. It went through a hole in the

_____. The ranch was near a busy

road. The calf headed for the road. It was in danger!

Two cowboys rode after the calf. They wanted to

bring it back to _____.

The cowboys rode up next to the calf. They

_____ turned it back. The calf tripped

and fell. We hoped its leg wasn't _____. The

cowboys _____ picked up the calf and

brought it home. The calf was fine.

26

At Home: Have children write two sentences with two
vocabulary words in each sentence.

Book 2.1/Unit 1
The Roundup at Rio Ranch   6

A Horse Named Buck

Carefully, the pilot walked up to Buck. "Buck, will you please give me a ride to town?" the pilot asked. The pilot climbed gently onto the horse. This time Buck did not move.

All of the cattle looked on in surprise. "Why are you giving him a ride?" one of them asked Buck. "You never give anyone a ride."

"No one ever said please before," said the horse.

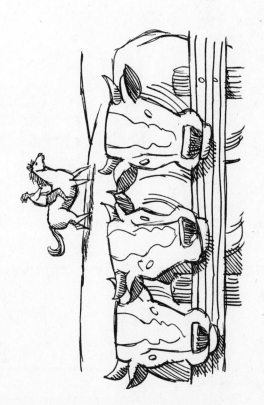

At Home: Have children draw another picture to go along with the story.

4

No one could ever ride the horse named Buck. He was too wild!

The cattle stood by the fence, watching him. "Will anyone ever ride Buck?" one of them asked.

One day a pilot came to the farm. "My plane is stuck in mud near a river. I must get it out," he said. "Can that horse give me a ride to town?"

The Roundup at Rio Ranch McGraw-Hill School Division

"No one can ride Buck," said the farmer.

"May I try?" asked the pilot. Within a minute the pilot was lying on the ground. Nothing was broken.

"I'm sorry the horse threw you," said the farmer as he tied Buck to a fence post with a rope.

"I have one more idea," the pilot said. "I must ride in safety."

Story Comprehension

Think about "The Roundup at Rio Ranch." Then answer these questions.

1. Who is José, and where does he live?

   _____

   _____

   _____

2. In the story, where does José go? Who does he go with?

   _____

   _____

   _____

3. What happens when José gets left behind?

   _____

   _____

   _____

4. Do you think José will grow up to be good cowboy? Why?

   _____

   _____

   _____

4 Book 2.1/Unit 1
The Roundup at Rio Ranch

At Home: Help children to summarize the story in their own words.

27

Use an Index

Use the **index** shown here to help you answer the questions. This index is from a book about ballet.

Barre, 65
Classes, 67, 79
Classical ballet, 34, 67, 102
Costumes (illustrations), 45
Injuries, 88
History of ballet, 5–6
Jumps (photos), 45–47
Music, 56

Positions, of the feet, 3–5, of the
    arms and legs, 7–9
Rehearsals, 77–79
Scenery, 22, 45, 90
Schools, 65
State theaters, 34–39, 61
Swan Lake, 54
Teachers, 23

On the line, write the subject and the page number or numbers where the answer might be found.

1. Where could I find out what the first ballets were like?

   _____

2. Where could I find out what ballet costumes look like?

   _____

3. Where could I find out about music composed for ballet?

   _____

4. Where could I find out about positions of the arms in ballet?

   _____

5. Where could I find photographs of ballet jumps?

At Home: Ask children to make up two more questions about the index above.

Long *o* and Long *i*

Circle the word that names each picture.

1. bow   pin

2. soap   same

3. no   yes

4. send   find

5. sky   sea

6. bottle   boat

7. deep   high

8. store   toe

8 Book 2.1/Unit 1
The Roundup at Rio Ranch

At Home: Help children to list three more words with the long **i** sound and three more words with the long **o** sound.

29

Name _____ Date _____ **Practice** **30**

Long Vowels

A. Choose the word that completes the sentence. Write the word on the line.

bay	my	bee	blow

1. We dock our boat in a small _____.

2. I can _____ out all the candles.

3. Have you ever been stung by a _____?

4. She gave me a goldfish for _____ birthday.

B. Draw a line from each sentence to the word that completes it. Then write the word.

5. You can see my teeth when I _____.   peas

6. The _____ sails down the river.   boat

7. She cannot _____ her ring.   smile

8. Would you like _____ or carrots?   find

At Home: Challenge children to use as many of the following words as they can in a single sentence: **I, say, eat, home, most, slow.**

Book 2.1/Unit 1
The Roundup at Rio Ranch   8

Make Predictions

Pretend each picture is from a story you are about to read. What do you think the story will be about? Underline the sentence.

1.
    a. Tom helps wash the car.
    b. Tom learns how to change a tire.
    c. Tom learns how to drive.

2.
    a. Baby birds eat worms.
    b. Baby birds build a nest.
    c. Baby birds learn to fly.

3.
    a. The family is going to the beach.
    b. The family is going shopping.
    c. The family is going to the library.

4.
    a. Lauren goes to school.
    b. Lauren scores a goal.
    c. Lauren is unhappy.

5.
    a. Chris does homework.
    b. Chris bakes a cake.
    c. Chris has a birthday party.

5   Book 2.1/Unit 1
The Roundup at Rio Ranch

At Home: Ask children to give their reasons for the predictions they made for each exercise.

31

Context Clues

Sometimes the other words in a sentence can help you figure out the meaning of a new word. These clue words can come before or after an unknown word.

Read each sentence. Then circle the meaning of the underlined word.

1. Peter and Maria put the dirty dishes in the sink. Peter got out the soap. Then he <u>washed</u> the dishes.

   run very fast   clean with soap and water

2. We saw a big <u>cactus</u> in Bob's garden. It had been growing there for fifty years.

   a kind of plant   a large dog

3. The blue paint from the brush <u>dripped</u> onto the floor. There were blue spots of paint all over the floor. Tom quickly put the brush in the sink.

   to fall in drops   to dance

4. Sue wanted to <u>mix</u> the sugar and the butter together first. She put them in a bowl and went to get a spoon.

   to jump up and down   to blend or put together

5. Sarah and Tony petted the <u>shaggy</u> dog. The dog had long brown hair and big ears.

   smooth and clean   covered with long hair

At Home: Ask children to explain the meaning of three new words in a story by using clue words in the same sentence or surrounding sentences.

32

Book 2.1/Unit 1
The Roundup at Rio Ranch

5

Short Vowels; Long Vowels

Circle the word that names each picture. Write the word.

1.

snake   cat

_____

2.

baby   tuba

_____

3.

leaf   coat

_____

4.

comb   fork

_____

5.

tire   bat

_____

6.

big   man

_____

7.

pie   lock

_____

8.

spoon   bell

_____

9.

sun   mom

_____

9 Book 2.1/Unit 1
Welcome to a New Museum

At Home: Play a riddle game with children. For example, say: "I am thinking of something that rhymes with cat. It is black and has wings." (bat)

33

Vocabulary

artist	body	famous	hour	life	visit

Choose a word from the box to finish each sentence.
Write the word on the line.

1. The park closes in one _____.

2. The _____ made a beautiful painting.

3. We are going to _____ my uncle in another state.

4. The old horse has had a very long _____.

5. We all know that very _____ singer!

6. My cat has hair all over its _____.

34

At Home: Have children write a story using three of the vocabulary words.

Book 2.1/Unit 1
Welcome to a New Museum 6

A Great Artist's Day

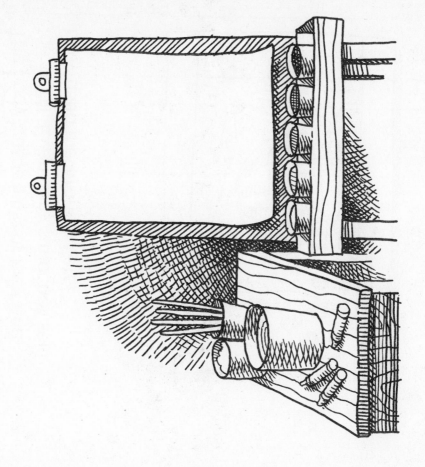

Lila looked around the room.
Everywhere she saw the children's paintings. Suddenly, she noticed Lucy's pictures.

Lucy tried to hide. She was afraid that Lila would think her paintings were funny, too!

But Lila did not laugh. She smiled. She cheered.

"What lovely colors! What great shapes! The student who painted this picture is a great artist," she said.

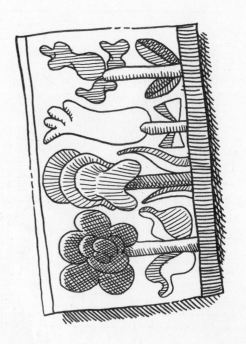

At Home: Invite children to draw a picture using unusual shapes and colors.

4

Lucy loved to paint. She waited for art class to paint flowers, trees, houses, and skies all hour long.

Some kids thought her paintings were funny. They thought Lucy's pictures did not look like real life. The body was too big or the head too small. Even Lucy's teacher said Lucy used the wrong colors.

Welcome to a New Museum McGraw-Hill School Division

One day there was a knock on the classroom door. It was Mr. Hugo, the principal. With him was his sister.

"Class, I would like you to meet my sister, Lila," he said. "She is a painter. She is here for a visit.

"Lila Hugo?" asked the art teacher. "You are a famous artist!" It was true! Lila was well-known for her paintings.

Story Comprehension

Think about what you read in "Welcome to a New Museum." Then answer these questions.

1. Name three things you can see in the Museum of African American History.

_____

_____

_____

2. What do the flags in the museum stand for?

_____

_____

3. Why is it important for people to visit the museum?

_____

_____

_____

4. Who are Katrina and Frederick? How did they help the museum?

_____

_____

_____

4 Book 2.1/Unit 1
Welcome to a New Museum

At Home: Have children tell about other museums they know.

35

Use the Internet

No two **search engines** will give you the exact same results. Using different **search engines** will give you more complete results. Search engines sometimes confuse words and give you **web sites** that aren't related to what you need.

Study the two different lists of search results. Both engines were given the subject "bubble making tools."

Search Engine **Chugalug**

1. <u>Soapy Pump—Bubbles!!</u>
   Endless bubbles with this air pump.
   http://www.soapypump.com/

2. <u>Glycerine Globes—Make Ten Foot Bubbles</u>
   The mail order kit you must have—$19.95.
   http://www.tenfootbubbles.com/

3. <u>Bubble Trouble—More Bubbles Than Ever</u>
   You'll be buried in bubbles. The best bubble soap ever. http://www.bubbletrouble.com/

Search Engine **Sherlock Look**

1. <u>Bubby Brewster Football</u>
   For fans of our Bubby, E-mail too.
   http://www.bubbybrewster.com/

2. <u>Bubbles You Can't Break</u>
   Add this powder to your bubbles.
   http://www.ironbubble.com/

3. <u>Tools For The Handyman</u>
   The finest tools for work around the house.
   Rock bottom prices. Send for our catalog.
   http://www.toolscheap.com/

Pretend you were looking for ways to create huge soap bubbles. Select four search results that would help you from the two lists above. Write the web addresses on the lines.

1. _____

2. _____

3. _____

4. _____

Make Predictions

You **predict** something when you try to guess what might happen next. Make predictions about the people in "Welcome to a New Museum."

1. Visitors will read the names of great Africans and African Americans. How will they feel? What do you predict?

   _____

   _____

2. How do you predict Frederick and Katrina will feel at the end of their visit to the museum?

   _____

   _____

3. Frederick has grown up. He brings his children to the museum. What will he say? What do you predict?

   _____

   _____

4. What do you think it was like for Mae Jemison to be the first African American woman in space?

   _____

   _____

At Home: Have children make believe that they visited the museum in this selection. Have them write a letter to a friend explaining some of the things they saw.

Story Elements

The **characters** are the people in the story. Tell what you know about the characters who visit the museum in "Welcome to a New Museum."

1. Characters: _____

2. What I know about them: _____

_____

The **setting** is where and when a story happens. Write details from the story under each heading.

3. Setting:

_____

_____

4. What do people see?

_____

_____

_____

5. What do people hear?

_____

6. Where is it?

_____

7. What do people learn about African American people?

_____

_____

_____

8. Things kids like to visit:

_____

_____

_____

_____

At Home: Help children think of a museum that they would like to create.

Context Clues

To figure out the meaning of words you don't know, you can use other words in the sentence or story as clues.

Look for clues to help you figure out the meaning of the word in dark print. Then underline the correct meaning of the word from the two choices below.

1. The **artist** drew a beautiful picture of the sailboat in the water.

   a. a person who draws or paints very well

   b. a person who likes to sail

2. The **statues** of the men and women in the museum look just like real people from long ago.

   a. a real person from long ago

   b. make-believe figures of people that look real

3. Although all the pictures in the show were pretty, only one could win first **prize**.

   a. something you buy in a story

   b. something you win

4. To make the mold, the artist put wet, **sticky**, paper that could not fall off over Joe's face.

   a. something that feels like glue

   b. something that is very dry

At Home: Encourage children to make a list of three new words they find in a story. Help them use word and picture clues to figure out the meanings of the words.

39

Inflectional Endings

Adding the endings **-s,-es,-ed,** or **-ing** to a word can change its meaning.

Read each sentence. Then complete the sentence with one of the words from the list below it.

1. Yesterday all the students _____ about the class trip.

   talk   talks   talked   talking

2. We are _____ to see our grandparents today.

   hope   hopes   hoping   hoped

3. Now Will _____ the flour and water together in the bowl.

   mix   mixes   mixing   mixed

4. All the children _____ to the pool and jumped in

   the water.

   rush   rushes   rushing   rushed

5. We all _____ eating breakfast.

   like   likes   liking   liked

6. The family were _____ leaves.

   rake   rakes   raked   raking

At Home: For each question above, have children make up a sentence using one of the inflections not chosen as the answer.

Unit I Vocabulary Review

A. Match each word with another word or phrase that has the same meaning. Write the letter of the definition on the line.

1. carefully _____   **a.** thought

2. searched _____   **b.** looked for

3. answered _____   **c.** kindly

4. idea _____   **d.** not death

5. gently _____   **e.** replied

6. life _____   **f.** watchfully

B. Read each sentence. Choose a word from the box that completes the sentence. Write your answer on the line.

lucky	different	crawls	fence

1. A baby _____ on the floor.

2. I don't like this hat. I want a _____ hat.

3. The girl found a penny. She is _____.

4. The horse jumped over the _____.

At Home: Have children choose four of the words above and use them in a story.

Unit I Vocabulary Review

A. Write **T** for **True** or **F** for **False** next to each sentence below. If a sentence is false, explain why.

____ **1.** An hour is shorter than a minute. _____

_____

____ **2.** A broken clock needs to be fixed. _____

____ **3.** A hundred is more than ten. _____

____ **4.** To hurry means to go very slowly. _____

_____

B. Find the following words in the word search below.

homework	parents	garden	cattle

```
b e r t u y t n e r t o p e n i m a p i n m
g o p u t r e s i b h u j e t r y l a k p l
a r e t y v e d f u y g h o m e w o r k r y
r f r e w p i o n v u j i o p v e r e p e c
d j e c d c a t t l e i i n u n o o n u n o
e k p u e h u i x z i e r t g r e e t y u t
n c e r t i h o p l u t f r e i d p s e d s
```

/ü/ *oo, ue, ew*

Circle the word that names the picture. Write the word.

1.

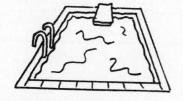

pool   pal

_____

2.

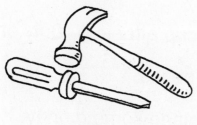

knew   chew

_____

3.

tools   cool

_____

4.

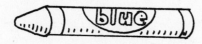

blue   glue

_____

5.

bloom   room

_____

5 Book 2.1/Unit 2
Lemonade for Sale

At Home: Have children make up nonsense rhymes
using words with the /ü/ sound.

43

Vocabulary

Write words from the box to finish the letter.

announced empty melted poured squeezed wrong

Dear Sally,

It is very hot. Today we sold lemonade. We

_____ the lemons ourselves. We got a lot of

_____ paper cups. Then we _____

to everyone that we were ready to sell. Lots of people

came. We _____ cup after cup. Only one

thing went _____ . The ice _____ !

Still it was lots of fun. We made some money. You

should try it.

                              Your friend,

                              Anne

The Great Pancake Contest

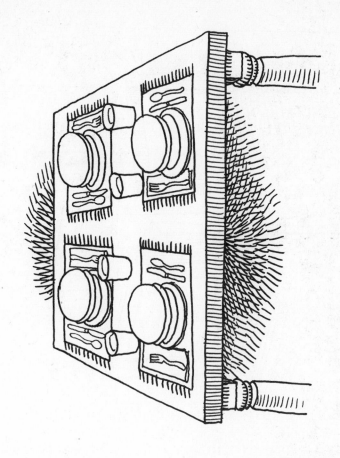

eaters left. Sue could eat lots of food! I was so full my face was blue. But I squeezed in a few more bites.

"Is anything wrong?" Mr. Thomas asked. "You two don't look so good."

"No more," we said together.

"Tim and Sue, the winners!" Mr. Thomas announced. "And their prizes are these medals and...more pancakes!"

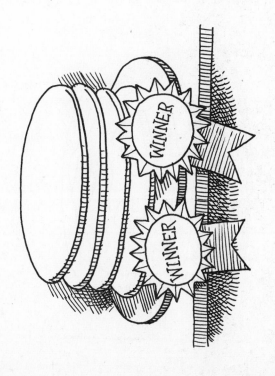

At Home: Have children come up with their own fun ideas for raising money for their school or another good cause.

4

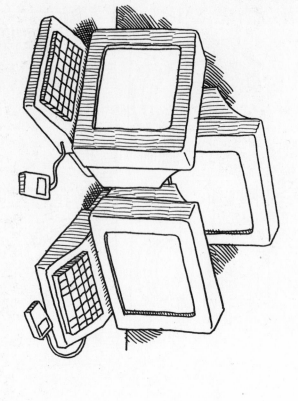

"We have to raise money," Mr. Thomas *announced*. "Any ideas?"

"How about a pancake contest!" I yelled.

And that day it was decided. We would ask our families and friends to give the school money for each pancake we ate! Then we could buy new computers for the school.

2

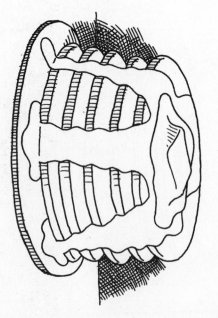

"Great," said Mr. Thomas. "You will have the contest next Tuesday."

When Tuesday came, I made sure my stomach was *empty*. I needed room for a lot of pancakes. I could smell the *melted* butter in the pan. Mr. Thomas *poured* the batter by the spoonful. Then we started eating the first pancakes.

"Keep them coming," I said. I poured syrup over my plate.

3

44b

Story Comprehension

Think of the things that happen in "Lemonade for Sale."
Number the sentences to show the order in which things
happen in the story.

_____ The children decide to sell lemonade.

_____ On Thursday, hardly any people buy lemonade.

_____ On Monday, the children set up the lemonade stand.

_____ Children have enough money to fix the clubhouse.

_____ On the first day, many people buy lemonade.

_____ Jed juggles near the lemonade stand.

At Home: Have children retell the story in their own
words.

Read a Graph

A **pictograph** represents numbers with pictures. Usually the pictures are symbols for the numbers as well as the things being counted.

The pictograph below represents the number of pets that students in various classes had in their homes. Notice that each symbol or picture of a pet stands for 5 pets of that type.

Pets Owned by the Students of the Mountain School

= 5 cats

= 5 dogs

Use the pictograph to answer the questions.

1. Which class had the most dogs for pets? _____

2. Which class had the smallest number of cats? _____

3. Which class had more cats than dogs? _____

4. There are some symbols that show only part of a cat or dog.

   Does that mean the students had only part of a pet? _____

5. What does the partial pet symbol mean? _____

   _____

At Home: Ask children to write another question based on the pictograph.

46

Book 2.1/Unit 2
Lemonade for Sale

5

/ü/ oo, ue, ew

Circle the word that completes the sentence. The answers have the same ending sound as in z**oo**, ch**ew**, and gl**ue**.

1. Mom is cooking _____.

stew

drew

few

2. The wind _____.

blew

new

drew

3. The police looked for a _____.

glue

clue

Tuesday

4. The cow said _____.

boo

moo

toot

5. The bicycle is _____.

threw

few

new

5

Book 2.1/Unit 2
Lemonade for Sale

At Home: Have children make up a story using these
/ü/ words.

47

/ü/ oo, ue

Circle the word that completes the sentence. Then write the word on the line.

1. He sat on a _____.

   stool   food   soon

2. We have paper and _____ for art class.

   true   glue   clue

3. The sky was _____.

   blue   zoom   due

4. I ate it with a _____.

   due   spoon   boot

5. The sun, the _____, and the stars are in the sky.

   tool   cool   moon

6. Look for _____ in the backyard!

   glue   true   clues

7. I put my _____ on my feet.

   clues   blues   shoes

8. That is false! It is not _____.

   true   you   boot

Problem and Solution

Think about the story "Lemonade for Sale." Put a **P** next to each sentence that tells about a problem. Put an **S** next to each sentence that tells about a solution.

1. _____ The clubhouse is falling down.

2. _____ The children do not have enough money for repairs.

3. _____ The children decide to earn money for repairs.

4. _____ The children plan to sell lemonade for the money they need.

5. _____ Each of the children does something to help the lemonade sales.

6. _____ People stop coming to the lemonade stand.

7. _____ Jed is drawing people away from the lemonade stand.

8. _____ The children have Jed join them.

8 Book 2.1/Unit 2
Lemonade for Sale

At Home: Have children identify alternate solutions
to the problem statements above.

49

Prefixes

A prefix is a word part that can be added to the beginning
of some words. The prefix **re-** means "again."

re + open = **re**open

Reopen means to open again.

Underline the word with the prefix **re-** and circle the prefix.
Then write the meaning of the word on the blank line.

1. This lemonade isn't sweet enough, so I will remix a new batch
   with more sugar.

   _____

2. After the pool is cleaned, it will be refilled with clean water.

   _____

3. When her car stopped running, Ms. Lopez tried to restart it.

   _____

4. After Tom wrote his book report, he reread it.

   _____

5. Before she mailed the birthday card, Meg rechecked the
   address.

   _____

6. When dinner was over, I removed all the plates from the table.

   _____

At Home: Help children begin a chart to record any
word they find that begins with the prefix **re-**. After
each word children should write its meaning.

50

Book 2.1/Unit 2
Lemonade for Sale

6

/ou/ *ow, ou* and /oi/ *oi, oy*

The b**oy** j**oi**ned the cl**ow**n in the f**ou**ntain **ou**tside.

Write the word from the box that completes the sentence.

loud	joyful	how	boil	round

1. The table is _____, not square.

2. I asked _____, not why.

3. The children were _____, not quiet.

4. We were _____, not sad.

5. The water will _____, not freeze.

⬜ 5 Book 2.1/Unit 2
A Letter to Amy

At Home: Have children say words that rhyme with those they wrote.

51

Vocabulary

Read each sentence. Choose a word from the box that means almost the same thing as the underlined word or words. Write the word on the line.

candles	corner	glanced	repeated	special	wild

I. <u>Again</u>, the bird <u>said</u> the boy's name.

_____

2. The animals in the jungle were <u>not gentle</u>.

_____

3. Sharon lit the <u>tall sticks of wax</u> with a match.

_____

4. Let's meet at the <u>place where John Street and Main Street meet</u>.

_____

5. Peter <u>quickly looked</u> at the sign.

_____

6. That is <u>not an ordinary</u> shirt.

_____

At Home: Ask children to rewrite the sentences with the words they chose as answers.

52

Book 2.1/Unit 2
A Letter to Amy
6

Oh, Brother

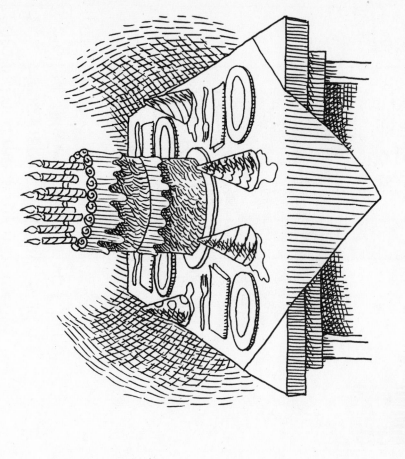

Suddenly, Nora noticed the cake in the corner. Then she *glanced* at Tommy. "Tommy!" she shouted. Tommy had eaten all the roses off the cake.

"I'm sorry," Tommy cried.

Sally looked at Nora. "Don't be mad. I have a brother just like Tommy. But I still love him."

The two girls laughed. "Oh, brother!" they said together.

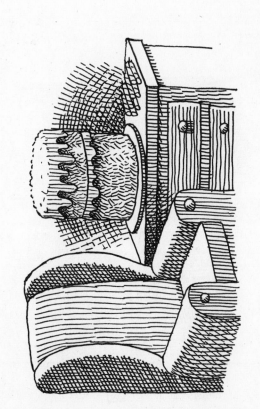

At Home: Have children think of things that they would like to have at their own birthday party.

4

"My birthday is coming," said Nora. "Can I have a big party?"

"Don't forget to ask Tommy," said her mother. Tommy was Nora's brother.

"He will spoil my *special* day!" said Nora. "He is too *wild*. He will run around and tease my new friend!"

"He is just a small boy," said her mother. "He will be sad if you do not ask him."

A lot of people came to the party. Nora's mother put the cake and *candles* in a *corner* so they would be safe.

Nora played with her new friend Sally. All the while, Tommy ran around the two girls. "Sally, Sally, Sally!" he *repeated* as he ran around Nora and Sally.

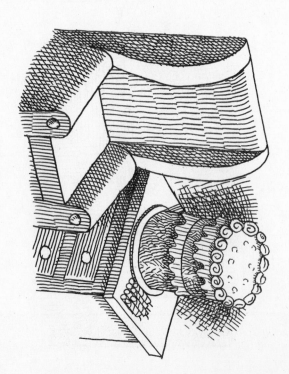

Story Comprehension

Read each question. Fill in the circle in front of the answer.

1. Who did Peter write a letter to?

   ○ his mother   ○ the boys   ○ Amy

2. Why did Peter write the letter?

   ○ to tell the boys about a camping trip
   ○ to invite Amy to his birthday party
   ○ to tell his mother about a meeting at school

3. When was Peter's party?

   ○ Friday at 3   ○ Tuesday at 5   ○ Saturday at 2

4. What happened to the letter when Peter went to mail it?

   ○ The wind blew it out of Peter's hand.
   ○ Peter lost the letter.
   ○ Peter left the letter at home.

5. Who did Peter bump into when he was chasing the letter?

   ○ Amy   ○ the boys   ○ a dog

6. How did Amy get the letter?

   ○ Peter handed it to her.
   ○ Peter mailed it to her.
   ○ Peter's mother brought it to Amy's house.

6 | Book 2.1/Unit 2
A Letter to Amy

At Home: Encourage children to discuss Peter's mixed-up feelings about inviting Amy to his birthday party.

53

Mail a Letter

Read the following paragraph. It describes step-by-step how mail is delivered.

> First, a truck takes the letter to the local post office. Then the postal workers sort the letters. Next, the carriers deliver the mail to the addresses shown on the envelopes. Then a person picks up his or her mail. Finally, the letter is opened.

Look at the illustrations. Put them in the correct order using the numbers 1–5, with 1 being the first step in the mailing process and 5 being the last.

 ___

 ___

 ___

 ___

 ___

At Home: Ask children to make up a story about someone mailing a letter.

Book 2.1/Unit 2
A Letter to Amy
5

/ou/ *ow, ou* and /oi/ *oi, oy*

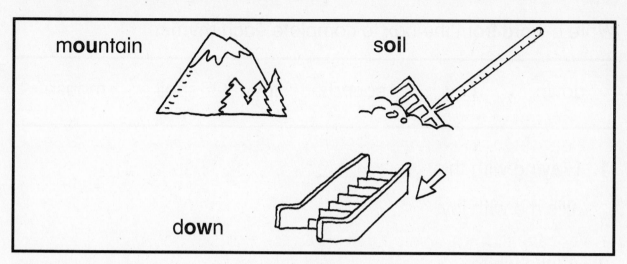

mountain

soil

down

Read each word. Then unscramble the letters to make a
word that rhymes.

1. soil   lio   _____

2. gown   nclwo   _____

3. blouse   soehu   _____

4. join   inco   _____

5. found   onusd   _____

6. noise   ysbo   _____

6

Book 2.1/Unit 2
A Letter to Amy

At Home: Have children recite a sentence for each
word they write.

55

/ou/ *ow, ou;* /oi/ *oi, oy;* /ü/ *ew*

Write a word from the box to complete each rhyme.

down	flew	sound	toy	spoil	mouse

1. Playing with this _____

   fills me with joy.

2. A little white _____

   lives under my house.

3. Would you frown

   if you fell _____?

4. The wind blew

   and the birds _____.

5. The howling _____

   was made by a hound.

6. Wrap the food in foil

   or else it will _____.

Make Inferences

Read the riddles. Then write the place name that solves each riddle.

1. I watch the monkey. Then I
   see the seals in their pool.
   Where am I?

   _____

2. When the bell rings, I sit down.
   I look on my desk and open
   my reading book. Where am I?

   _____

3. I feed the birds. I play
   on the swings. Then I sit
   on a bench and eat lunch.
   Where am I?

   _____

4. When the lights go down,
   I stop talking. Everyone is eating
   popcorn and watching the show.
   Where am I?

   _____

5. I jump in the water and swim
   to the side. The lifeguard waves
   to me. Where am I?

   _____

5 Book 2.1/Unit 2
A Letter to Amy

At Home: Ask children to identify specific clues that
helped them answer each riddle.

57

Compound Words

Two small words make up a **compound word.** You can learn the meaning of a compound word from the meaning of each small word in it.

rain + coat = raincoat
Lee wore her **raincoat** in the storm.

Circle the compound word. Then write the two small words in the compound word.

1. I will go to Willie's birthday party on Saturday.

   _____

2. Someone found my book and returned it to me.

   _____

3. Anne put all the letters in the green mailbox on the corner of Oak Street.

   _____

4. All the children played outdoors because it was so warm.

   _____

5. Lisa found a starfish in the sand at the beach.

   _____

6. Everybody came to our class play on Friday.

   _____

At Home: Help children to list as many compound words as they can think of. Ask them to circle the small words in each compound.

58

Book 2.1/Unit 2
A Letter To Amy
6

/âr/ *are*; /ôr/ *or, ore*; /îr/ *ear*

Circle the missing letters. Then write them.
Read the word.

1.

    ear   ore

    st_____

2.

    are   ear

    h_____

3.

    or   are

    c_____n

4.

    or   are

    sp_____

5.

    ore   ear

    c_____

5   Book 2.1/Unit 2
The Best Friends Club   **At Home:** Have children use each written word in a
sentence.   59

Vocabulary

Choose a word from the box to finish each sentence. Write the answers in the puzzle.

president	promise	rules	allowed	leaned	whispered

Across

2. Marie is the —— of the club.

5. Mark —— the name in Tom's ear.

6. We are not —— to leave until 3 o'clock.

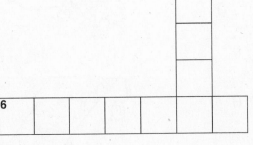

Down

1. Judy —— to the left to see better.

3. Our club has only four ——.

4. I —— to bring a gift to the party.

The Car Club

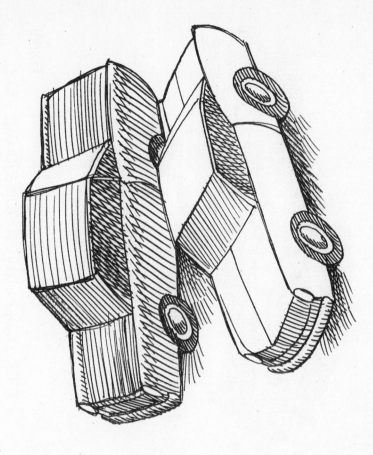

"Max's club sounds like fun," Jim said. "We can play on Beth's porch and play with Lisa's cars, too."

"But you are breaking your *promise* to be in my club," Mike said.

"I do not like your *rules*," said Jim.

"You can be *president* by yourself."

"I see what you mean," said Mike.

"Care if I join your club?"

"Bring your cars!" said Max.

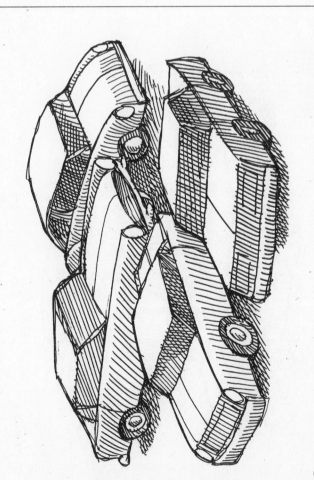

At Home: Ask your child why Max didn't want to join Mike's car club. Why might have Mike wanted to be president? Why did Jim say he would join Max's club?

4

60a

"Let's start a toy car club," said Mike.
"Great," said Jim. "I have a lot of toy cars. Can we ask Lisa, too?"
"No girls *allowed*," said Mike.
"Why *not*?" asked Jim.
"Because I said so," said Mike.
"Who are you to say so?" asked Jim.
"I am the *president* of the club," said Mike.

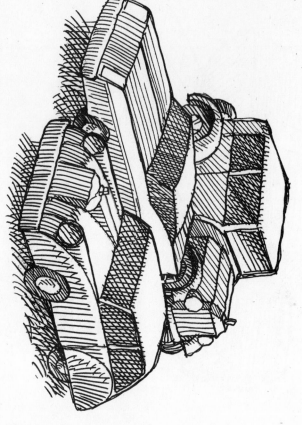

The Best Friends Club McGraw-Hill School Division

"Well, can I ask Max?" Jim asked.
"Yes," said Mike, "he has even more cars than I do."
Jim *leaned* over near Max and told Max the *rules*. Then he asked,
"Do you want to join our club?"
"No," Max *whispered* to Jim.
"Mike is a mean boy. Beth and Lisa are more fun. I like to share my cars with them. We will start our own club."

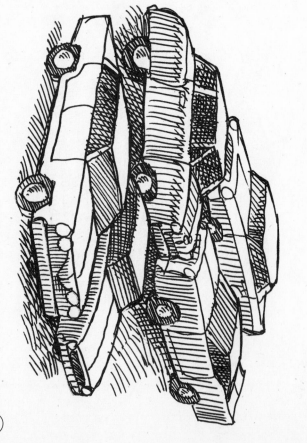

Story Comprehension

Think about "The Best Friends Club." Then fill in the chart below.

1. Main Characters (who):
   _____
   _____

2. Problem:
   _____
   _____
   _____
   _____

3. What happens:
   _____
   _____

4. What happens next:
   _____
   _____

5. Ending:
   _____
   _____

5 Book 2.1/Unit 2
The Best Friends Club

At Home: Have the children use the chart when retelling the story.

61

Use a Diagram

Study the **diagrams** below. They show part of a string game called cat's cradle. One person loops string around his or her fingers to create a pattern of X shapes inside a circle. Another person changes the pattern to a pattern called the soldier's bed.

    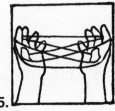

1. 2. 3. 4. 5.

Study these diagrams and answer the following questions.

1. How many fingers does the string loop around in the first step?

_____

2. What part of the string is pinched in step 2?

_____

3. How many people are needed to change the pattern? _____

4. Why do you think the final design is called the soldier's bed?

_____

_____

/âr/ *are*; /ôr/ *or, ore*; /îr/ *ear*

Complete each sentence with a word from the box.

bare	clear	born
year	hear	snore

1. Fill in the day, month, and _____ .

2. He was walking on his _____ feet.

3. Listen to the sleeping man _____ .

4. When were you _____ ?

5. Can you _____ the singing birds?

6. The water is so _____ .

/âr/; /ôr/; /îr/; /ou/; /oi/; /ü/

Choose the word that completes the sentence. Write the word on the line.

share	tore	near	bow	bloom
threw	ground	storm	now	toys

1. I _____ the ball.

2. I dropped my coat on the _____.

3. There is a rain _____ outside.

4. You and I can _____ this sandwich.

5. I fell and _____ my pants.

6. The dog barks when I come _____.

7. We clap as the clown takes a _____.

8. Many flowers _____ in the spring.

9. I want to play with my _____.

10. I want it _____, not later.

Problem and Solution

Think about "The Best Friends Club." Read the
sentences below that tell about problems. Then write a
solution for each problem.

Problems	**Solutions**
1. Harold and Lizzie want people to know where their club is.	_____ _____
2. The club president has to make up the rules.	_____ _____
3. Harold wants both Lizzie and Douglas as friends.	_____ _____
4. "Lizzie's Club" is the wrong name for the new club.	_____ _____
5. Douglas invites everyone in his class to his party. Lizzie is not in his class.	_____ _____

At Home: Have children offer other solutions to some
of the problems in the story.

Prefixes

A prefix is a letter or letters that are added to the
beginning of a word to change its meaning.
The prefix **re-** means "again."
The prefix **un-** means "not" or "opposite of."

repaint	unhappy	redo	revisit	untied

Read each sentence. Then fill in the blank with one of the
words from the box. Circle the prefix in the word. Write the
meaning of the word on the line.

I. Max will _____ his report to make it better.

_____

2. Her cat has not come home and Ellen is very _____.

_____

3. The boy will trip because his shoelaces are _____.

_____

4. We will _____ the sign with blue flowers.

_____

5. Next month we will _____ the library and take out
more books.

_____

At Home: Help children identify words with the prefixes
re- and **un-**. After they write the words, ask them to
circle the prefix in each word.

Book 2.1/Unit 2
The Best Friends Club
5

/är/ *ar;* /ûr/ *ir, ur, er*

Circle the missing letters. Then write them to complete the word. Read the word.

1.

ar   ur

st_____t

2.

ur   er

h_____t

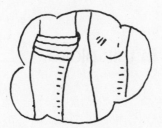

3.

ar   ir

c_____cle

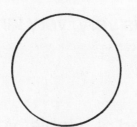

4.

er   ir

k_____nel

5.

ar   ir

c_____t

5

Book 2.1/Unit 2
Jamaica Tag-Along

At Home: Have children name other words with these letter combinations.

67

Vocabulary

Read the clues. Write the correct word from the box next to each clue.

edge	form	building	busy	giant	repair

1. If something breaks, this is what you can do to it. _____

2. You might go to school in this place. _____

3. This is something that is very, very large. _____

4. When you get to the end of a table, you are here. _____

5. You do this to shape something. _____

6. If you have a lot to do, you are this. _____

At Home: Ask children to make up riddles about things they do when they are playing.

The Snow Girl

"What is that?" I asked.

"I made a snow girl," she said.

"What is that black spot by her eye?" I asked.

"She is crying because her brother will not play with her."

"Come help me," I smiled.

Jackie took the black spot away.

"No more tears!" she said.

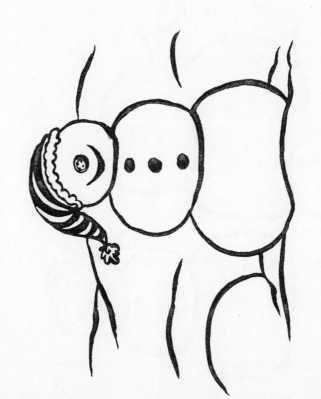

4

2

I was walking out the front door of our *building* when I heard my mom yell, "Take your sister with you!"

But I did not want her with me. It was the year's first snow and I was going to be *busy* making a *giant* snowman. It would be bigger than any snowman ever seen. The snow was just cold enough to *form* the perfect snowman.

Jamaica Tag-Along McGraw-Hill School Division

"Don't go walking out while I work," I told my sister as we turned to go outside.

"Can't I help you?" she asked.

"No, Jackie," I said. "You are a girl. You cannot build snowmen."

I saw that she was hurt. But right then the *edge* of the snowman began to break. I had to *repair* it. Then I heard a boy say, "That is good!"

3

Story Comprehension

Think about the story "Jamaica Tag-Along." Number the pictures to show the order in which things happened in the story.

☐ Jamaica builds a sand castle.

☐ Berto wants to play, too.

☐ Ossie says, "No."

☐ Jamaica wants to play.

☐ Jamaica says, "No."

☐ Jamaica says, "Yes."

6 Book 2.1/Unit 2
Jamaica Tag-Along

At Home: Have children retell the story in their own words.

69

Read a Diagram

A **diagram** is often used to show how something works.
Study the diagram below. It shows a system that heats
water with the sun.

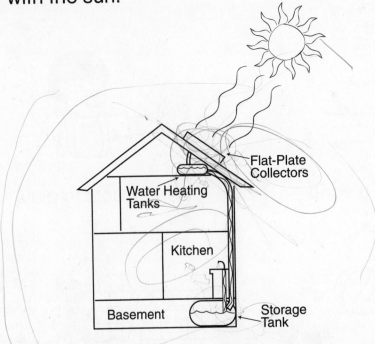

Use the diagram above to answer the questions that follow.

1. What heats the water up on the roof? _____

2. What is the name of the device on the roof that is heated by

   sunlight? _____

3. Where is the water stored after it moves from the roof?

   _____

4. Where is the water used in the house? _____

At Home: Ask children to think of other ways that solar
power could be used.

/är/ ar; /ûr/ ir, ur, er

Circle the word that names the picture.
Then write the word.

1.
(burn)
turn

burn

2.
fern
stern

_____

3.
dirt
shirt

_____

4.
car
jar

_____

5.
turn
churn

_____

At Home: Have children use two words from this
page in a sentence.

/är/; /ûr/; /âr/; /ôr/; /ü/

Use these words to answer the riddles.

girl	star	few	school	fur	stare
herd	horn	pair	car	food	bird

1. I am where you go to learn. What am I? _____

2. I am the hair that grows on animals. What am I? _____

3. I am a child, and I am not a boy. What am I? _____

4. I look at something for a long time. What do I do? _____

5. Blow in me and I will make music. What am I? _____

6. I am a large group of cows. What am I? _____

7. I am not very many. What am I? _____

8. I twinkle in the night sky. What am I? _____

9. I fly in the sky. What am I? _____

10. I am two of something. What am I? _____

11. You eat me. What am I? _____

12. People drive me. What am I? _____

At Home: Have children write a riddle for the word corner.

72

Book 2.1/Unit 2
Jamaica Tag-Along 12

Make Inferences

Read the story. Then answer each question. Use a complete sentence.

> Billy stepped up to bat. He wished that he could just sit on the bench. He was only playing this game because his brother needed another player. The ball flew by him twice, and twice he swung at it. Then Billy just closed his eyes and swung one more time. CRACK! Billy couldn't believe it. He watched the ball go over the fence.

1. What sport is Billy playing?

_____

2. How do you know this?

_____

_____

3. How does Billy feel about this game?

_____

_____

4. How do you think Billy feels at the end?

_____

_____

4 Book 2.1/Unit 2
Jamaica Tag-Along

At Home: Ask children to name the clues they found in the story to help them answer questions 3 and 4.

73

Compound Words

If you know the meaning of each smaller word in a **compound,** you can figure out the meaning of the word.

Complete each sentence with one compound word from the box. Then write each small word in the compound on the line.

anything basketball	everybody	fireplace bookcase

1. Please put all the books in the _____.

   _____

2. Our _____ team will play again on Friday.

   _____

3. _____ is coming to see our class play.

   _____

4. It's nice to sit in front of the warm _____.

   _____

5. I don't have _____ to do after school.

   _____

At Home: Help children list compound words that identify objects in their homes and identify the two small words in each compound.

74

Book 2.1/Unit 2
Jamaica Tag-Along

10

/är/; /ûr/; /ôr/; /îr/; /oi/; /ü/

Read each clue. Then complete the puzzle.

north	market	noise
dirt	true	room

ACROSS

2. A loud _____

3. Not false

5. A place where you shop

DOWN

I. Plants grow in it

2. Not south but _____

4. Part of a house, like a bed _____

6
Book 2.1/Unit 2
Sharks

At Home: Have children use each of the words in a
sentence.

75

Vocabulary

Choose a word from the box to complete each sentence. Write the words on the lines.

| trouble | understand | afraid | chew | danger | lessons |

1. The teacher asked the children not to _____

   gum in class.

2. Bobby did not _____ the math problem.

3. Sam and Jan are not _____ of spiders.

4. We can learn many _____ from animals.

5. She broke one of the rules. Now she is in _____.

6. Many animals are in _____ of dying out.

76

At Home: Ask children to make up a crossword puzzle using the vocabulary words.

Book 2.1/Unit 2
Sharks
6

THE BIG ROAR

"What should we do?" cried Drew.

"Take out the food," said Jordan.

"We don't *understand*," said the others.

"That is my stomach roaring. I need to boil some soup and *chew* on some bread!" Jordan said.

"Why didn't you tell us?" they asked. Jordan's stomach roared again. "I just did!"

At Home: Have children talk about a camping trip they went on or would like to go on.

Four girls were hiking in the park. They were nearing Blue Mountain when they heard a roar.

"Are there bears here?" asked Drew. "If so, I am *afraid*."

"We are in no *danger*," said Jordan.

But the others did not hear her.

"In a science *lesson* we learned that if you see a bear you should never turn and run," said Marla.

Roar!

The girls stood very still.

"That sounds like *trouble*!" said Dorrie.

"Don't worry!" said Jordan.

But everyone ignored her.

Story Comprehension

Read these sentences about "Sharks." Write **Yes** beside each fact in the story. Write **No** if the sentence does not tell a fact from the story.

Is it a fact from the story?

_____ **1.** Scientists study sharks.

_____ **2.** Learning about sharks might help people fight off

sickness.

_____ **3.** Movies are sometimes made about dolphins.

_____ **4.** Sharks help balance the number of animals in

the sea, and this helps our food supply.

_____ **5.** Sharks die when they lose their teeth.

Read the two sentences below. Decide which is a correct sentence about the story. Draw a line under the sentence.

Sharks can be very useful to people.

I am afraid of sharks.

6 Book 2.1/Unit 2
Sharks

At Home: Have children make a generalization about
shark hunting.

77

Use a Bar Graph

The graph below will show you the sizes of different types of sharks. Your job is to draw the bars.

Complete the graph. The types of sharks are listed with their size in feet. The length of each bar depends on the size of the shark. The first one is done for you.

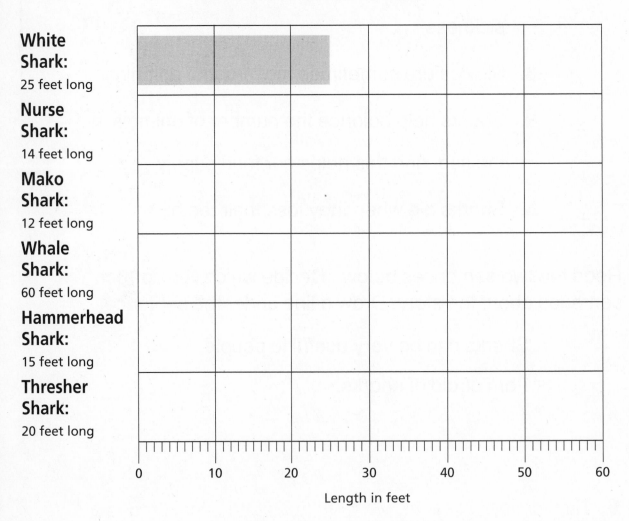

Different Lengths of Sharks

White Shark: 25 feet long

Nurse Shark: 14 feet long

Mako Shark: 12 feet long

Whale Shark: 60 feet long

Hammerhead Shark: 15 feet long

Thresher Shark: 20 feet long

0   10   20   30   40   50   60

Length in feet

At Home: Ask children to make a bar graph similar to the one above that compares the heights of family members or friends.

78

Book 2.1/Unit 2
Sharks
5

Make Inferences

Read the riddles. Think about the clues and then write the
answers. Use the words in the box.

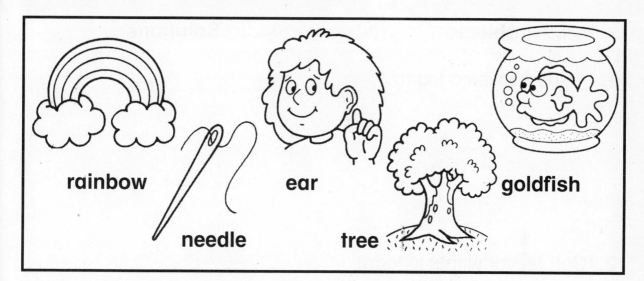

rainbow   ear   goldfish

needle   tree

1. I have a drum, but it is not for tapping.

   I am an _____.

2. I have an eye, but I cannot see.

   I am a _____.

3. I have a bark, but I cannot bite.

   I am a _____.

4. I am a kind of bow that cannot be tied.

   I am a _____.

5. I am covered in gold, but I am not worth a lot of money.

   I am a _____.

5   Book 2.1/Unit 2
Sharks   **At Home:** Challenge children to use clues to create
riddles of their own.   79

Problem and Solution

Read the problems from "Sharks." Then write the solution for each problem.

Problems	Solutions
1. A shark loses a tooth.	_____ _____ _____
2. Carl Meyer wants to learn about the tiger shark.	_____ _____ _____
3. Sharks are in danger of disappearing.	_____ _____ _____
4. People who do not know about sharks fear them.	_____ _____ _____

At Home: Have children discuss other misunderstood topics that can be helped by more understanding.

Compound Words

Two smaller words make up a **compound word.**
Knowing the meaning of each small word helps you
understand the meaning of the compound word.

Circle the compound word in each sentence. Then write
the two small words in each compound word.

1. People must understand more about sharks and how they live.

   Did you know that a hammerhead shark has eyes on the side

   of its head? Most sharks do not want to hurt people. But

   sometimes they think a person in the water is a sea animal.

   _____

   _____

   _____

2. Anne and Frank love to eat hot oatmeal. This food is always

   good to eat when it is cold outside. After eating, they carry their

   plates to the kitchen. There they wash them in a dishpan.

   _____

   _____

   _____

18 Book 2.1/Unit 2
Sharks

At Home: Have children write three original
sentences that use compound words.

81

Prefixes

A word part that is added to the beginning of a word to change its meaning is called a **prefix**.

The prefix **re-** means "again."

The prefix **un-** means "not" or "opposite of."

Add the prefix **re-** or **un-** to the beginning of the underlined word. Then write the meaning of the new word.

1. We ____made our beds with warmer blankets.

_____

2. When I ____folded the package, I could not find the colored

balls that were inside.

_____

3. Let's ____load all the boxes from the truck and carry them inside

the house.

_____

4. We must ____lock the door to get inside the house.

_____

5. The bird will ____appear in our city next spring when the weather

is warm again.

_____

At Home: Help children make up new words by adding the prefix **re-** or **un-** to each of the following: **turn** [return], **place** [replace], **tie** [untie], and **friendly** [unfriendly].

Unit 2 Vocabulary Review

A. Choose the word from the box that completes each sentence.

repair	empty	wrong	special

1. My birthday is a _____ day.

2. Dad tried to _____ the broken bike.

3. We were surprised that the box was _____.

4. Is my answer right or _____?

B. Answer each question.

squeezed 1. If you <u>squeezed</u> some pieces of an orange, what would come out?

_____

melted 2. What would you do if your ice-cream <u>melted</u>?

_____

president 3. What makes someone a good <u>president</u>?

_____

rules 4. How many <u>rules</u> does your class have?

_____

8 Book 2.1/Unit 2
Unit 2 Vocabulary Review

At Home: Have children write a story about a busy person.

83

Unit 2 Vocabulary Review

A. Answer **Yes** or **No** to each question.

1. Can <u>candles</u> light a room? _____

2. If you <u>glanced</u> at something, would you look at it for a long

   time? _____

3. Is the <u>edge</u> of a table in the middle? _____

4. Is <u>scared</u> another word for afraid? _____

5. If you <u>chew</u> something, do you use your teeth? _____

6. Can you go inside a <u>building</u>? _____

B. Look for context clues to figure out the meaning of the underlined vocabulary word. Then define each vocabulary word.

1. I <u>poured</u> milk into the glass. But not all of the milk flowed into the glass. Some of it spilled on the floor. _____

2. The teacher said the letters of the alphabet, and the students <u>repeated</u> the letters after her. _____

3. I am very <u>busy</u>. I take singing lessons, play baseball,and am in the Science Club. _____

4. I waited for you at the <u>corner</u> of Green and King Streets.

   _____

At Home: Have children circle the clues that helped them to figure out the meaning of each word in Exercise B.

Silent Letters

Write the words. Then say each word. Circle the silent
letter or letters in each word.

l	b	k	w	g	h	gh

1. could _____

2. knee _____

3. sign _____

4. thumb _____

5. high _____

6. tow _____

7. white _____

8. lamb _____

9. know _____

10. light _____

11. which _____

12. should _____

12 Book 2.1/Unit 3
Arthur Writes a Story

At Home: Have children think of a word that rhymes
with each of the words above.

85

Vocabulary

Choose a word from the box to complete each sentence.
Write the word on the line.

decided	float	important	library	planet	proud

1. Jenny went to the ___ to find some books.

_____

2. Paul's and Carol's kites ___ in the wind.

_____

3. Lily ___ to help clean up the park.

_____

4. Baseball is very ___ to Lou.

_____

5. Jade's parents were very ___ when she won.

_____

6. Earth might be the only ___ with life on it.

_____

86

At Home: Ask children to illustrate four sentences and write another sentence to go with them.

Book 2.1/Unit 3
Arthur Writes a Story
6

The Important Planet

I should just throw out all my books and grow food, it thought.

Then it had a better idea. The planet decided to call the food planet.

"I have some books for you!" the library planet told the food planet.

The food planet checked out every cookbook ever written.

And, thanks to two important planets, everyone ate well that day!

At Home: Discuss with children why it is important to be yourself. How can you help others and still be yourself?

4

86a

Once there was a planet called the library planet. The people of the library planet were proud of their books. They had all the books that were ever written.

One day the library planet saw another planet float by. "Who are you?" the library planet asked.

"I am the food planet. I grow all the food people need. Without me, people could not live."

Arthur Writes a Story McGraw-Hill School Division

They began to talk. "What do you do?" asked the food planet.

"I have every book ever written," the library planet said.

"People cannot eat books," said the food planet. "People can eat food. I know I am more important."

The library planet felt very sad.

Story Comprehension

Think about "Arthur Writes a Story." Write **T** if the statement is true about the story. Write **F** if the statement is not true about the story.

_____ 1. Arthur is a student.

_____ 2. D.W. is Arthur's mother.

_____ 3. Arthur is working on a music project.

_____ 4. Arthur has to write a story for class.

_____ 5. At first, Arthur writes about his puppy.

_____ 6. Arthur writes several different stories.

_____ 7. The Brain is Arthur's teacher.

_____ 8. Penelope is Arthur's friend.

_____ 9. Arthur's class likes his story about the puppy.

_____ 10. Arthur's class does not like his song and dance story.

_____ 11. Arthur got a gold sticker for his story.

_____ 12. Francine wrote a song for her story.

Use a Dictionary

When you look up a word in a **dictionary,** you have to remember the order of the letters in the alphabet. If you check the guide words, you'll know if you're on the right page.

Write the following two lists of words in alphabetical order. If the first letter of two words is the same, look at the second letter.

A-B-C Order		**A-B-C Order**	
made	_____	pedal	_____
elephant	_____	meek	_____
rock	_____	moon	_____
race	_____	wrap	_____
clamp	_____	sleep	_____

88

At Home: Write down six words, and have children put them in alphabetical order.

Book 2.1/Unit 3
Arthur Writes a Story
10

Silent Letters

Answer each riddle. Then circle the silent letters in each answer.

knee	write	right	talk	sign
thumb	wrong	lamb	light	knob

1. You do this when you say something. _____

2. This is the fattest finger on your hand. _____

3. This is what you kneel on. _____

4. You do this with a pencil and paper. _____

5. This tells you what to do on a road. _____

6. This is not your left. _____

7. This is a baby sheep. _____

8. A lamp gives you this. _____

9. This is on a door. _____

10. When something is not correct. _____

10 Book 2.1/Unit 3
Arthur Writes a Story

At Home: Ask children to write one more riddle with a word that has a silent letter for the answer.

89

Silent Letters

Finish each sentence below. Circle the word that completes the sentence. Then write the answer.

1. Most people sleep at _____.

   night   knew   written

2. Do you _____ her name?

   high   bright   know

3. I _____ to school, but he takes the bus.

   weigh   walk   knock

4. I _____ him a letter.

   high   wrote   talking

5. I could not untie the _____.

   knot   flight   knee

6. Baby sheep are called _____.

   limbs   rams   lambs

7. My _____ is part of my leg.

   knock   arm   knee

8. I _____ on the telephone.

   talk   walk   wink

At Home: Have children illustrate one of the sentences above.

Book 2.1/Unit 3
Arthur Writes a Story   8

Fantasy and Reality

Read the story. Draw two pictures about Bear showing something that could not happen in real life. Then complete the sentences.

Why Bears Have Short Tails

It was winter and Bear was hungry. Fox led him to a hole in the ice. The hole was filled with fish. Fox told Bear to stick his long tail into the hole. "Fish will bite your tail. When you feel them, pull up your tail. The fish will hang on." Bear waited and waited. He never felt a bite. After a long time, he stood up. When he took his frozen tail out of the water, it snapped and fell off. And that is why bears have short tails.

This is not like real life because

_____

_____

_____

This is not like real life because

_____

_____

_____

4   Book 2.1/Unit 3
Arthur Writes a Story

At Home: Ask children to tell what words let them know the story was not like real life.

91

Context Clues

You can use **context clues** to help you figure out the meaning of an unknown word.

Write the clue words that help you figure out the meaning of the word in dark print. Then write **before** or **after** to show if the clue words come before or after the word.

1. At night I like to look at the stars in the sky through my **telescope**. The telescope makes things that are far away seem closer.

   _____

   _____

2. I saw a bright ball of gas through my telescope. It had a tail. I think this is called a **comet**.

   _____

   _____

3. I like books about the stars. Someday I hope to be an **astronaut**. An astronaut is a person who is trained to travel in space.

   _____

   _____

4. We saw the largest planet in the sky. This planet is one of the brightest objects in the sky. It is called **Jupiter**.

   _____

   _____

At Home: Encourage children to identify two new words in a favorite story or book and to figure out the meanings of the words using context clues.

92

Book 2.1/Unit 3
Arthur Writes a Story

8

/ər/ er

Read the words below. Listen to the sound the letters **er** make in each word.

cov**er**   anoth**er**   und**er**

Think about "Best Wishes, Ed." Then read the sentences. Choose a word from the box that completes each sentence and write the word on the line.

winter	letter	smaller	under
larger	over	hammer	another

1. Ernest the whale is _____ than Ed the penguin.

2. The iceberg is getting _____.

3. Ernest the whale swims _____ the water.

4. Ed writes a _____ in the snow.

5. Clouds float _____ Ed's head.

6. During the story it is _____.

7. Ed makes _____ friend.

8. The ice breaking sounded like a _____.

At Home: Have children illustrate one of the sentences they completed.

Vocabulary

Choose words from the box to finish the letter. Write the words on the lines.

climbed	couple	drifted	half	message	notice

Dear Louis,

Thanks for sending me the _____ about the camping trip. I have been to Mountain Park. I _____ to the top of the mountain with my mother. It took us a _____ of hours. We were very high up. A cloud _____ by right next to us. Coming down was easy. It took us only _____ as long as going up. My legs got very tired. But I didn't even _____ it until we stopped. I hope we can climb again next summer.

Your friend,

Pete

At Home: Ask children to write the message that Louis might have written to Pete about the camping trip.

Book 2.1/Unit 3
Best Wishes, Ed

6

Message from the Sun

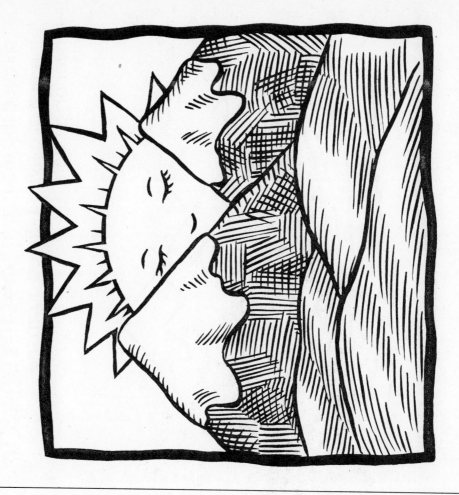

...that night, slept under a big tree.

In the morning, I felt someone tap my fingers. It was the sun!

"Good morning," the sun said.

"Do you see now why I set early in winter? It is so people like you will get the sleep they need!"

"Thank you!" I said. I happily walked home. The sun kept me warm the whole way.

At Home: Talk with children about times of the year and when the sun sets during those times. How does the sun affect our days?

4

Did you ever notice that the sun sets early in winter? Did you ever wonder why?

One day I set off to find out. I started walking toward the sun. When it hid behind a mountain, I climbed the mountain. When it hid at the end of a river, I drifted down the river on a boat.

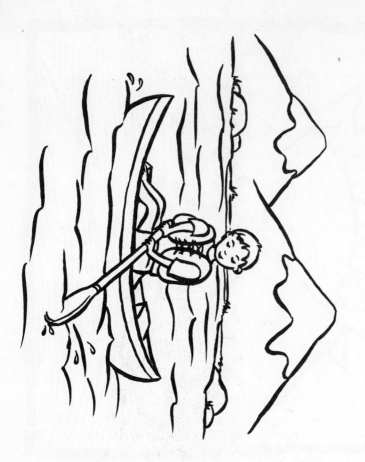

I could never catch up. I would travel half of the distance to the sun, and then it would get dark!

After a couple of weeks, I gave a bird a message to give to the sun. It said, "Please tell me why you set so early in the winter!"

Story Comprehension

Think about "Best Wishes, Ed." Who said each sentence?
Color the answer.

1. Ernest does not even notice penguins.

2. I will be here all my life.

3. Will you write a letter for me?

4. I do not know how to fly.

5. I have lots of things to do besides helping penguins.

5 Book 2.1/Unit 3
Best Wishes, Ed

At Home: Have children tell at least one other thing
Ed said during the story.

95

Use an Encyclopedia

Study the sample **encyclopedia** page shown below.
Some encyclopedia entries have **cross references**.
These point you to related entries you might like to read.

Poland — Police

Poland is a country in central Europe. It borders on the Baltic Sea. Its name comes from a tribe of people called the Polane. They lived over a thousand years ago in that area. Poland has rich natural resources and is famous for its industry.

Polar bear is a large white bear found near the Arctic Ocean. A full-grown bear can be over nine feet tall and weigh close to 1,000 pounds. Polar bears are great hunters and strong swimmers. (See also *Bears*)

Police are government workers who make sure people obey the law. Police control traffic and try to find out who committed crimes. They also help out during natural disasters like floods or tornadoes. There are city police and state police. Each group enforces the laws, but state police serve cities that don't have their own police force. Police officers are sometimes called *cops*. It is thought the word comes from their copper badges.

Use the entries above to answer the following questions.

1. How much does a polar bear weigh? _____1000 pounds_____

2. The word for Poland comes from what tribe of people?

   _____Poline_____

3. What kind of cities do state police serve? _____

   _____

4. Where is the country of Poland found? _____

5. What other entry does the entry under *Polar bear* tell you to

   read? _____

/ər/ er, /ən/ en, /əl/ le

Write the word that answers each riddle.

| apple | open | letters | flower | seven | table |

1. You can eat on it. You can put things on it. What is it?

_____

2. This pretty thing can be many different colors. It can grow in a garden or in a pot. What is it?

_____

3. You can eat this fruit or bake it in a pie. What is it?

_____

4. This number comes before eight. It is one more than six. What number is it?

_____

5. A, B, and C are three of these. You write them every day. What are they?

_____

6. When the door is not closed, what is it?

_____

At Home: Help children make up a riddle that has an answer that rhymes with **flower**.

/ər/, /ən/, /əl/; Silent Letters

Circle the word that completes each sentence. Then write the word.

1. The ocean is full of me. I am _____.

   water   powder

2. I am a pencil. Use me to _____.

   wring   write

3. Cook dinner in me. I am an _____.

   oven   right

4. People do what I say. I am a _____.

   sign   spider

5. After dinner, let's take a _____.

   walk   talk

6. Light me when the power goes out. I am a _____.

   handle   candle

7. Let's _____ to the top of the mountain!

   climb   lamb

8. I come after seven and before nine. I am _____.

   eight   weight

Cause and Effect

Read the story. Then read each sentence below that tells something that happened in the story. Write why each thing happened.

In the spring, penguins pile up rocks to make a nest. Here, each mother lays an egg. The mother and father keep the egg warm until it hatches. Then, the mother leaves to catch fish for her baby. When she comes back, it is the father's turn to catch fish. After the baby gets bigger, the father will teach the young one how to swim and dive. Then the baby can catch its own fish.

1. The penguins pile up rocks.

_____

2. The mother and father keep the egg warm.

_____

3. Mother leaves her baby penguin.

_____

4. Father teaches the young penguin how to swim and dive.

_____

4 Book 2.1/Unit 3
   Best Wishes, Ed

At Home: Have children tell about a time when they watched something new happen. Why did it happen?

99

Context Clues

Sometimes other words in a sentence or a story can help you figure out the meaning of a new word. These words are called **context clues.** They can come before or after the unknown word.

Choose the word or group of words that help you figure out the meaning of the word in dark print. Write these context clues on the line.

1. A big wave washed on the beach and **splashed** everyone there.

    _____

2. **Penguins** are birds who live where there is lots of ice and snow.

    _____

3. When the big tree fell over into our yard, it made a big **cracking** noise.

    _____

4. Because he had no one to play with, Ed the penguin felt very **alone**.

    _____

At Home: Ask children to write three sentences about a favorite story. They should use three new words that are explained by context clues in their story.

Book 2.1/Unit 3
Best Wishes, Ed
4

Short *e: ea*

Say the words. What sound do both words have in common?

ready   **fea**ther

The sound made by the letters **ea**.

bread	ready	breath	leather
weather	steady	breakfast	head

Read the story below. Then choose a word from the box to write on each line.

The _____ was very cold that morning.

Johnnie had a hot _____. He had a piece of

_____ with jam and some eggs. He put a

warm hat on his _____. Then he went outside

and put the _____ saddle on his horse. It was

so cold, he could see his _____.

Finally, he was _____. But the ice and

snow were slippery. Johnnie shouted, "_____"

to his horse. It would be a day of hard work!

At Home: Have children pronounce each of the words they wrote. Then have them underline the letters that make the sound of short **e** in each word.

101

Vocabulary

Choose a word from the box that has the opposite or the same meaning as the underlined word. Write the word on the line.

arrive	early	finish	record	rush	success

I. If you <u>start</u> a game, be sure to _____ it.

2. There's no <u>hurry</u> to get there, so don't _____!

3. Please don't be <u>late</u>. Try to be _____.

4. When you _____, call and let me know you have <u>gotten there</u>.

5. Karla set a world _____ because she was the <u>first and only</u> woman to climb the mountain.

6. Our team is not a <u>failure</u>. It is a _____.

At Home: Ask children to make up a short story using the words in the box.

102

Book 2.1/Unit 3
The Pony Express

6

Waiting for Beth

Soon Freddy and his father were running out the door.

"We must rush!" said Freddy's father.

At the train station, they ran all the way to Beth's train. She watched them come.

"I think you two just broke my record!" laughed Beth. And together they all walked slowly back home.

At Home: Talk with children about a time someone they loved came to visit. What did they do together?

4

102a

Monday morning Freddy woke up early. He called to his father's room. "Daddy, when is Beth going to arrive at the train station?"

Freddy's father snored, "Not for hours! Go to bed, sleepy head!"

But Freddy could not sleep. He was too excited to see his sister. He read about her in the newspaper.

It was about her great success as a runner for her school. Freddy was proud. And soon he would see her!

He waited and waited. He made himself something to eat. Then he called out, "Daddy? Is it still hours till Beth gets here?"

"Oh no!" cried his father. "I overslept! Quick! Finish your breakfast!"

Story Comprehension

Answer the following questions about "The Pony Express."

1. What was the Pony Express?

_____

_____

2. Why did William Russell start the Pony Express?

_____

_____

3. What did the riders of the Pony Express carry?

_____

4. What were the riders on the Pony Express like?

_____

_____

5. What was the motto of the Pony Express?

_____

6. Why did the Pony Express stop after just a short time?

_____

_____

At Home: Have children write a short story about whether they would have liked being a Pony Express Rider.

Use a Telephone Directory

A **telephone directory** lists people and businesses in alphabetical order.

Study the sample page below. Use it to answer the questions that follow.

192	Hodges — Holmes

HODGES Catherine Near Rd Red Bank 555-9863
    Kenneth 1692 West Walnut Martinsville 555-2347
    P.C. 1324 Weston Rd Riverton 555-4376
HOFFMAN Nelson 45 Brushy Hill Rd Lambert 555-9898
    Michelle M 373 South St Remertown 555-3245
HOFFMANN SEE ALSO HOFFMAN, HOFMAN, HOFMANN

1. What is the phone number of P.C. Hodges? _555-4376_

2. What other spellings of Hoffmann are suggested? _____

_____

3. Pretend you're looking for someone named Hoffman. You

   don't know the first name. But you know the person lives in

   Lambert. Which Hoffman would you pick? _____

4. Suppose you're looking for someone named Holton. Would

   you find that person on this page? Why or why not?

_____

At Home: Ask children how many different people listed on this page have the last name Hodges.

Short *e: ea*

Write the word from the box that each statement describes.

ahead	bread	feathers	weather
heavy	lead	ready	leather

1. I am not fur, but I do cover some animals. What am I?

   _____

2. Sometimes I am sunny. Sometimes I am rainy. What am I?

   _____

3. I am in front of something or someone. What am I?

   _____

4. I am used to make a sandwich. Sometimes you feed me to the

   ducks. What am I? _____

5. I weigh a lot. What am I? _____

6. I am the black part of your pencil. What am I? _____

7. I am used for shoes, gloves, and saddles. What am I?

   _____

8. I want to do something now. I don't want to wait. What am I?

   _____

Book 2.1/Unit 3
The Pony Express

At Home: Ask children to find two more words with
the short **e** sound spelled **ea** and write them down.

Short *e;* /ər/, /ən/, /əl/; Silent Letters

Choose a word from the box to finish each statement.

leather	finger	high	straight	seven	sign

1. I am more than six and less than eight. I am _____.

2. I am not low. I am _____.

3. People make shoes out of me. I am _____.

4. I tell people things like "Stop" and "Exit." I am a _____.

5. I am not bent. I am _____.

6. You point with me. I am a _____.

Now draw a line from each question to the right answer.

7. I am a baby cow. What am I?   table

8. I am a very quiet voice. What am I?   calf

9. I can spin a web. What am I?   spider

10. You sit around me to eat. What am I?   whisper

At Home: Have children make up a riddle for the word saddle.

106

Book 2.1/Unit 3
The Pony Express

10

Fantasy and Reality

Think about "The Pony Express." Then read the story below. Circle the sentences that are **real,** and draw a line under the sentences that are **make-believe.** Then write two more sentences to finish the story. Write one real sentence and one make-believe sentence.

Johnnie Frye was a young rider. He was brave, fast, and tough. His horse had wings. He could fly through the air. Johnnie's horse was all different colors, like a rainbow. Together, Johnnie and his horse carried the mail. They rode in all kinds of weather. Sometimes they would drive. Other times they would take the train.

The Pony Express riders worked very hard at their jobs. After a little more than a year the Pony Express ended. Mail began to deliver itself.

Real _____

_____

Make-believe _____

_____

14 Book 2.1/Unit 3
The Pony Express

At Home: Have children rewrite the story using only the sentences they circled.

107

Synonyms

Synonyms are two words that have the same or nearly the same meaning.

The **angry** bears ran toward each other in the forest.
The **mad** bears ran toward each other in the forest.
Angry and **mad** are synonyms.

Read each sentence. Write a synonym for the word in dark print.

1. The mouse was too **small** to jump on the table and eat the cheese.

   _____

2. Meg was **sad** because she hurt her arm when she fell down.

   _____

3. My friend Ed and his family live in the log **cabin** in the woods.

   _____

4. Tom thought the picture of the pig riding a horse was **silly**.

   _____

5. Lisa picked the **tulips** from the garden and put them in a basket.

   _____

At Home: Encourage children to identify six words that describe objects in their home or school. Then ask them to substitute a synonym for each describing word.

108

Book 2.1/Unit 3
The Pony Express

5

Long *e: y, ey*

Read each group of words. Circle the word that has the same ending sound as ba**by** or monk**ey**. Then write the word on the line.

1. brown   money   horse

_____

2. hand   dog   silly

_____

3. nine   scary   book

_____

4. ready   purple   garden

_____

5. fountain   build   turkey

_____

6. honey   day   band

_____

6 Book 2.1/Unit 3
Nine-in-One, Grr! Grr!

At Home: Have children write a sentence for each word they wrote on the lines.

109

Vocabulary

Circle the word that answers the riddle. Then write the word on the line.

earth   forget   lonely   memory   mountain   wonderful

1. I am very tall and fun to climb.   _____

mountain   earth   sky

2. I am the ground under your feet.   _____

sea   earth   Mars

3. I help you think of something from the past.   _____

memory   think   say

4. I'm something that is very good.   _____

bad   forget   wonderful

5. I am the opposite of *remember*.   _____

forget   lonely   good

6. I am sad and all by myself.   _____

memory   lonely   happy

110
At Home: Ask children to use the vocabulary words to make a crossword puzzle.

Book 2.1/Unit 3
Nine-in-One, Grr! Grr!   6

Turtle's Gift

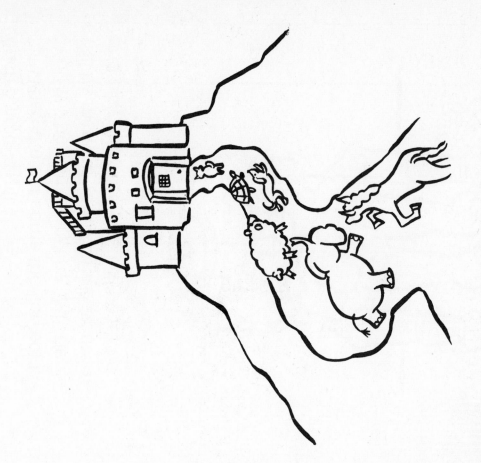

One day the turtle came. "You will be small and have a hard shell," said the lion.

"You gave those gifts to the ant and to the crab," the turtle said. "I would like to be wise."

"Very well," said the lion. "Those who are wise stay quiet so they can listen." That is why the turtle hears all but says nothing.

At Home: Have children imagine other animals coming to the lion for their gifts. What would he give them?

4

110a

2

Long ago there was a lion who
was king of all the animals on Earth.
Every year he came down from his
home on the mountain and gave
each animal a gift.

When the ant came the lion said,
"You will be very, very tiny. But there
will be many of you. You will work
and play together. You will never be
lonely."

Nine-in-One, Grr! Grr! McGraw-Hill School Division

When the monkey came, the lion
said, "You will be happy to hang by
your tail and jump from tree to tree."

Many more animals came for
gifts. All of the gifts were wonderful.
But the lion began to worry.

I am getting old, he thought. My
memory is not so good. Maybe I will
forget and give two animals the
same gift. That would never do.

3

110b

Story Comprehension

Think about "Nine-in-One, Grr! Grr!" Put an X by each sentence that tells about something that happened in this story.

_____   Tiger lived in the sky.

_____   The great god Shao knew everything.

_____   Tiger asks Shao how many cubs she will have.

_____   Tiger is sad after she talks to Shao.

_____   Tiger makes up a song to help her remember
           what Shao told her.

_____   Tiger forgets how to get home.

_____   Bird doesn't want Tiger to have nine cubs
           every year.

_____   Shao promises Bird he will change what he said to
           Tiger.

_____   Bird makes Tiger change her song.

_____   Tiger will have one cub every nine years.

At Home: Ask children how they would change the false statements on this page to make them true statements.

Use a Dictionary

A **dictionary entry** contains many different parts. Study the entry shown below. See if you can pick out each different part.

> **pup** **1.** a young dog; puppy. **2.** the young of some other animals, such
> as the fox, wolf, or seal. *The mother fox takes good care of her pup.*
> (pup) *noun, plural* **pups**

Complete the exercise based on the dictionary definition above.

1. entry word _____

2. definition #2 _____

_____

3. part of speech _____

4. plural form _____

5. pronunciation guide _____

6. example sentence for definition #2 _____

_____

At Home: Ask children to make up a sentence using
the first definition for "pup."

Long *e: y, ey*

Read the sentence. Then circle the word that ends in **y** or **ey** and completes the sentence. Write the word and circle the **y** or **ey** ending.

1. The _____ was in her carriage .

   bag   band   baby

2. Jean and Pat were very _____.

   happy   crying   purple

3. Tawana saved her _____.

   apples   money   birds

4. Don't _____; the rain will stop soon!

   eat   sleep   worry

5. The _____ loved to climb.

   truck   monkey   girl

6. There are four people in my _____.

   cave   family   foot

Long *e;* Short *e;* /ər/, /ən/, /əl/

Choose the word that completes each sentence.
Write the word on the line.

shiny	children	bread	apple	key
sneakers	sell	freeze	lead	weather

1. This gold ring is very _____.

2. The _____ wait for the school bus.

3. I pick an _____ from the tree.

4. I can't find one of my _____.

5. You need _____ to make a sandwich.

6. He opens the door with a _____.

7. We will listen to the _____ report so we will know what
to wear.

8. We will _____ water to make ice.

9. If you _____, we will follow.

10. Stores don't give things away; they _____ them.

At Home: Have children write a rhyming poem using at
least one of the words above.

114

Book 2.1/Unit 3
Nine in One, Grr! Grr!

10

Cause and Effect

A **cause** is the reason why something happens.
An **effect** is what happens.

Cause	Effect
Tiger wonders how many cubs she will have each year.	Tiger decides to visit Shao to learn the answer.

Read each cause. Then write its effect.

Cause	Effect
Tiger travels to the sky and speaks to Shao.	_____ _____
Tiger worries that she won't remember what Shao told her.	_____ _____
Bird doesn't want Tiger to have nine cubs each year.	_____ _____
Tiger sings the song "One-in-nine, Grr! Grr!"	_____ _____

4

Book 2.1/Unit 3
Nine-in-One, Grr! Grr!

At Home: Ask children what effect different numbers would have on both Tiger and Bird.

115

Synonyms

A word that means the same or nearly the same as another word is a **synonym**.

Look at the underlined word. Write a synonym for the underlined word from the words in the box.

jumped	shop	helpful
chilly	rested	dropped

1. In the fall the apples <u>fell</u> from all the trees.

   _____

2. Tim wanted to buy dog food in the pet <u>store</u> on Green Street.

   _____

3. After running hard in the five-mile race, Lucy <u>sat</u> on the bench.

   _____

4. The cat <u>leaped</u> from one branch to another branch in the tall tree.

   _____

5. After the sun went down, it became quite <u>cool</u> in the park.

   _____

6. The owner of the book store, Mr. Hernandez, is always very <u>nice</u> to me when I shop there.

   _____

At Home: Ask children to write three original sentences about a real or make-believe place. Then ask them to identify synonyms for three of the words in their description.

116

Book 2.1/Unit 3
Nine-in-One, Grr! Grr!   6

Long *e*; Short *e*; /ər/, /ən/, /əl/; Silent Letters

Complete each sentence using the words below.

bought	handle	honey	right	knew
seven	garden	cover	many	bread

1. I raised my hand because I _____ the right answer.

2. My mother _____ me a new coat.

3. We raise bees for their _____.

4. We made a _____ turn at the corner.

5. Joan has _____ cats living in her barn.

6. The _____ broke off the pitcher.

7. I helped plant the seeds in the _____.

8. Mother showed me how to bake _____.

9. Take the _____ off the box and look inside.

10. He had too _____ broken toys.

10 Book 2.1/Unit 3
Change for the Quarter

At Home: Help children make a list of other words
that have long e; short e; /ər/, /ən/, /əl/; and silent
letters.

117

Vocabulary

Read the sentences. Choose a word from the box that means almost the same thing as the words in parentheses. Write the word on the line.

collect	honor	join	order	pocket	worth

1. The mountains (meet with) the river at the town.

   _____

2. See if you have a dime in your (part of a coat).

   _____

3. The children (speak very well of) their grandparents.

   _____

4. Put the days of the week in the right (way of listing).

   _____

5. These cards are (how much they cost) ten cents each.

   _____

6. I'm going to (gather and keep) stuffed toys.

   _____

At Home: Have children write a new sentence for each vocabulary word.

Book 2.1/Unit 3
Change for the Quarter 6

Two to Collect

why don't you have them now?" I asked.

"I do! They are in the attic. I am going to look for them right now. Why don't you join me?" she said.

"Okay!" I said. "Families who collect together will always have something to share."

4

It's time to throw out some of these comic books," Mom said. "There is room for only a couple of them."

"But, Mom, I collect them," I said.

"I think you must have every comic book ever written," she said. "They must weigh a ton." Then she smiled. "I remember I used to be a collector, too."

asked.

"No, stamps," she said. "My father got lots of mail. He let me keep the stamps. I put them in order in a leather book. Some of the stamps were to honor people or countries. Once my father pulled a stamp out from his pocket for my birthday. It was worth a lot."

Story Comprehension

Write an **X** next to each statement that is true about
"Change for the Quarter."

1. _____ The 25-cent piece is getting a new look.

2. _____ Twelve new quarters will come out each year.

3. _____ The first five new quarters came out in 1999.

4. _____ New Jersey was one of the first five states.

5. _____ Some kids collect coins.

6. _____ Quarters cost a lot of money to make.

7. _____ Delaware was the first state to join the United States.

8. _____ New quarters will honor all 50 states.

9. _____ George Washington's head will be on the new quarter.

10. _____ The new quarter will be worth 50 cents.

11. _____ These new quarters are not to be spent.

12. _____ The eagle will not be on the "tails" side any more.

12 Book 2.1/Unit 3
Change for the Quarter

At Home: Have children start a collection. They can
collect coins, stamps, dried flowers, or bottle caps.

119

Choose a Reference Source

Study the uses of a dictionary listed below. Then study the uses of an encyclopedia. Use these guides to help you answer the questions.

Dictionary:

1. gives more than one definition if the word has more than one

2. tells you how to pronounce the word

3. tells you the part of speech each meaning has—example:
   lead (to guide someone) *verb*
   lead (a heavy metal) *noun*

4. may use the word in a sentence

Encyclopedia:

A. may break the topic down into its parts and fully explain them

B. may give facts and numbers related to the topic, as well as graphs and charts

C. may include maps, photos, and diagrams

D. may provide history of the topic

Choose the number or letter of the different uses shown above that would help you answer these questions.

1. What is the history of the Girl Scouts? _____

2. What part of speech is the word *funny?* _____

3. What countries surround Mexico? _____

4. How is the word *ragout* pronounced? _____

5. How many tons of gold are mined in Colorado? _____

At Home: Ask children which would be more helpful if they wanted to find out about the history of Texas, a dictionary or an encyclopedia.

120

Book 2.1/Unit 3
Change for the Quarter
5

Cause and Effect

Read the story about Grandma's biscuits. Think about what happened and why it happened.

"It's too lumpy," Grandma said to Ellen. She mixed in more water. Then she rolled out the dough on the table. "I like my biscuits the same size. Get me a glass," said Grandma. She turned the glass upside down to cut the biscuits. Then she put the tray of biscuits in the oven to bake. In twelve minutes the bell rang. Guess who was first in line for a biscuit? Ellen was!

Read each cause. Then write its effect.

Cause	Effect
The dough was too lumpy.	_____ _____
Grandma likes her biscuits the same size.	_____ _____
The biscuits had to bake.	_____ _____
Ellen liked hot biscuits.	_____

At Home: Ask children to name an event that happened in the classroom. Have them suggest probable causes for the event.

Fantasy and Reality

Reality means something that can happen in real life.
Fantasy means something that can't happen.

Read each sentence. If it could happen, write **reality** next
to it. If it could not happen, write **fantasy** next to it.

1. Horses can fly over your house. _____

2. A dog can jump on a chair. _____

3. A cat can talk to a person. _____

4. Elephants can walk in mud. _____

5. A rainbow has many colors. _____

6. Chairs can walk. _____

7. I can walk on a rainbow. _____

8. A cat can meow. _____

9. Frogs can go shopping. _____

10. Horses can run fast. _____

11. The moon is made of blue cheese. _____

12. A house can have many windows. _____

At Home: Ask children to write two sentences: one
fantasy and one reality.

122

Book 2.1/Unit 3
Change for the Quarter
12

Synonyms

Synonyms are words with the same or nearly the same meaning.

Read each group of words in column 1. Then draw a line to the word in column 2 that is a synonym for the word in dark print.

Column 1

1. the **tiny** mouse

2. the **shining** light

3. the **large** building

4. **run** down the hill

5. **lift** up the heavy books

6. the **happy** baby

7. the **playful** kitten

8. **sliding** down the hall

Column 2

1. big

2. glowing

3. raise

4. smiling

5. small

6. active

7. slipping

8. race

At Home: Encourage children to read a paragraph of a favorite story. Then ask them to identify synonyms for four of the words in the story.

Context Clues

Context clues are words in a sentence or story that help you figure out the meaning of a new word. Context clues can come before or after the unknown word.

Read each sentence. Look at the word in dark print. Then underline the clue words that help you figure out what the word in dark print means.

1. Rose stayed in bed because she had a bad **cold**.

2. I cooked the **stew** on top of the stove.

3. Pete put all the letters in the **mailbox**.

4. When our team won the baseball game we all **cheered**.

5. Lisa **painted** a picture of the birds in the park.

6. I can't **reach** the book because it's on a high shelf.

7. All the runners will take part in the **race**.

8. In the spring all the flowers in the garden will **bloom**.

124

At Home: Ask students to use each of the following words in an original sentence: bright, favorite, music. Remind them to include clue words that explain the meaning of the word.

Book 2.1/Unit 3
Change for the Quarter 8

Unit 3 Vocabulary Review

A. The same vocabulary word is used twice in each example below. Write the words from the box on the lines.

library	pocket	rush

1. I went to the _____ and took out a book. There are

   many books in the school _____.

2. I was late, so I had to _____ to school. We'll have

   to _____ if we want to get there on time.

3. I have some nickels in my _____. My jacket

   _____ is torn.

B. Read each sentence. Find a vocabulary word from the box that means almost the same thing as the underlined word. Write the word on the line.

couple	finish	notice

1. I have a <u>pair</u> of apples. _____

2. I didn't <u>see</u> her. _____

3. <u>Complete</u> your homework. _____

6 | Book 2.1/Unit 3
Unit 3 Vocabulary Review

At Home: Have children illustrate one of the sentences above.

125

Unit 3 Vocabulary Review

A. Write the correct vocabulary words in the sentences.

arrive	forget	order	important

1. Who is the most _____ person you can think of?

2. What time do you _____ at school?

3. Did you ever _____ your lunch?

4. Are the numbers 1, 2, 4, 3 in the right _____?

B. Find the words below in the word search.

drifted	lonely	message	earth	finish	worth

```
t v r e l l d r i f t e d s d m p l i z u t x m
e r e i t i l i m o o m i s e i n i t u t r e e
a u p i s i t u r e f i s n s i l o n e l y r s
r u a g i n g k m g s e g n i i t m i n g t e s
t u p j m p u i p n n n n w o r t h p w e e u a
h g u o j o e d p u i t r e n k o p e p e p t g
a i o g u p r r e d f r e w e o t n o i r o e e
g r t i n p i n h e r f i n i s h e n s r y v e
```

At Home: Have children make up a sentence using the words in Exercise B.

Book 2.1/Unit 3
Unit 3 Vocabulary Review 10

/ù/ oo

Write the letters **oo** to complete each word. Then say the name of each picture.

1.

c____k

2.

h____d

3.

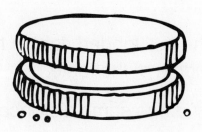

c____kie

4.

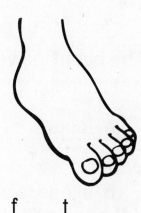

f____t

5.

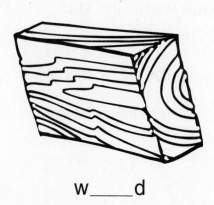

w____d

6.

h____k

6 Book 2.2/Unit 1
Charlie Anderson

At Home: Have children use each of the words they completed in a sentence.

127

Vocabulary

Read each sentence. Fill in the circle next to the meaning of the underlined word.

chocolate	clothes	middle	offered	roof	upstairs

1. Anna likes to eat chocolate cookies best.

   ○ **a.** a food

   ○ **b.** a sound

2. The man offered to fix the wall of the house.

   ○ **a.** said he would not

   ○ **b.** said he would

3. The baby had very wet clothes.

   ○ **a.** food

   ○ **b.** things to wear

4. The ball landed right in the middle of the table.

   ○ **a.** the same distance from each side

   ○ **b.** in the corner

5. My mother says never to climb on the roof.

   ○ **a.** the side of a building

   ○ **b.** the top of a building

6. Jack went upstairs to his room.

   ○ **a.** the floor above

   ○ **b.** the floor below

At Home: Have children write a story using the underlined words.

128

Book 2.2/Unit 1
Charlie Anderson
6

Luke and His Cat

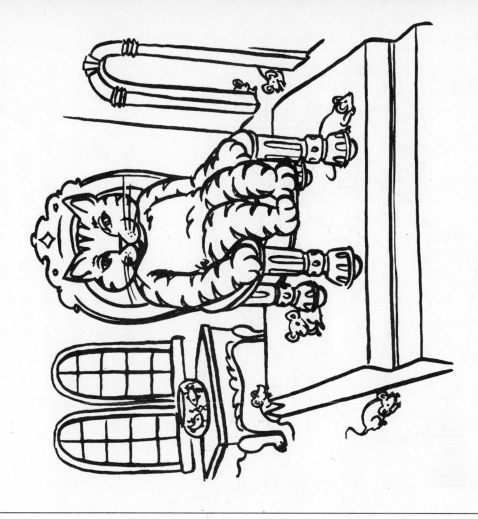

At the castle the king saw the boy coming with his cat. "Look!" he said. "Help is here!"

"Watch what my cat can do," Luke said. The cat ran upstairs. Soon, it came back with many mice.

After that the king asked Luke and his cat to stay. And they did, for a long, long time.

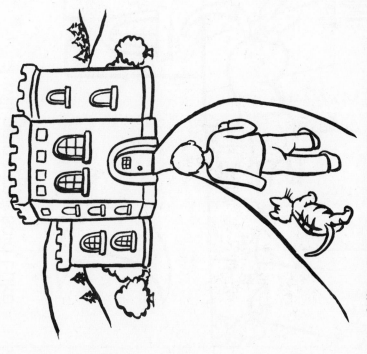

At Home: Discuss with children a time they have had a problem and how they solved it.

4

A long, long time ago there was a boy named Luke. Luke liked to travel from place to place.

One day, he came to a big house. "May I work here?" he asked the cook. The cook said yes!

The cook gave Luke a job and some new clothes. He also offered Luke some chocolate cookies and milk. Luke gave some of his milk to his cat. Then Luke went to sleep.

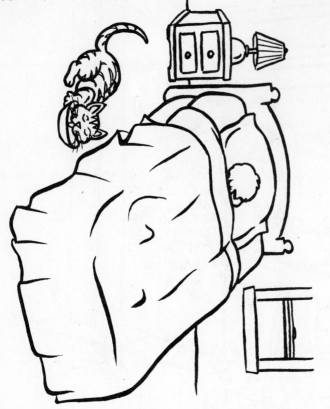

Charlie Anderson McGraw-Hill School Division

In the middle of the night the cat woke up. It went upstairs and onto the roof, looking for mice. But Luke knew his little friend would come back to him. It always did.

The next day the cook said, "Did you hear about the king? His castle is filled with mice. No cats want to catch them."

"I will help him," said Luke.

Story Comprehension

Think about the story "Charlie Anderson." Put an **X** next to each sentence that tells about something you found out in this story.

1. _____   Charlie is a cat.

2. _____   Sarah dresses Charlie in doll clothes.

3. _____   Charlie always sleeps in the woods.

4. _____   Elizabeth runs away with Charlie.

5. _____   Charlie has two homes.

6. _____   Sarah and Elizabeth are sisters.

7. _____   The girls take Charlie to visit their father.

8. _____   Mother helps the girls look for Charlie.

9. _____   Charlie's other name is Anderson.

10. _____   Charlie is loved by two families.

Use a Map

A **map** can be like a maze. Use a map to find your way through different roads and towns.

Follow the directions given below. Draw a line on the roads to show your path. To make sure you went the right way, answer the questions below the map.

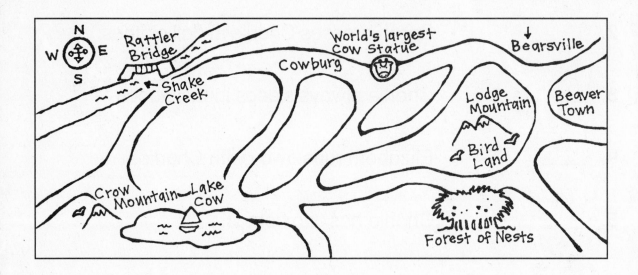

1. What mountain is near Beaver Town? _____

2. What forest is near Bird Land? _____

3. What landmark is near Cowburg? _____

_____

4. What crosses Snake Creek? _____

5. What body of water is found near Crow Mountain? _____

At Home: Show children a map of the area where you live. Point out landmarks and places of interest.

130

Book 2.2/Unit 1
Charlie Anderson

5

/ǔ/ *oo*

Name each picture. Write the word that has the sound of
oo as in **foot**.

1.

_____

2.

_____

3.

_____

4.

_____

5.

_____

5

Book 2.2/Unit 1
Charlie Anderson

At Home: Have children draw a picture that includes
at least three of the items that contain the letters **oo**.

131

/u̇/oo

Draw a line from each clue to the word it describes.

1. Make some food.		foot
2. Put a shoe on me.		hook
3. Hang up your coat on me.		soot
4. See something.		cook
5. Keep your head warm with me.		hood
6. Sweep a chimney and find me.		look
7. I come from trees.		book
8. You read me.		wood

At Home: Have children read a book to find other words that have the same sound as **oo** in woods.

132

Book 2.2/Unit 1
Charlie Anderson

8

Draw Conclusions

elephant   **whale**   **giraffe**   **tiger**

Read the riddles. What animal is it?
Write the name of the animal.

1. I breathe through a hole
    and swim in the sea.
    I'm as big as a ship.
    Can you guess me?
    Let's see!   _____

2. I can eat leaves from a tree,
    and I'm yellow and brown.
    I have a long neck
    to see all around.
    Who am I?   _____

3. You could ride on my back
    and climb down my long nose.
    Be sure to watch out for
    my big heavy toes!
    Guess who I am.   _____

4. I live in the wild,
    and I'm orange and brown.
    If you see many stripes,
    you know I'm around!
    Who am I?   _____

4 | Book 2.2/Unit 1
Charlie Anderson

At Home: Have children make up their own animal
riddles and share them. Discuss the words that
helped the children solve each riddle.

133

Antonyms

Antonyms are words that have the opposite or nearly the opposite meaning.

In each pair of sentences, a word in the first and a word in the second sentence are antonyms. Circle these words. Then write them.

1. The cat left the woods on a cold night.

   The cat sat in front of a warm fire.

   _____

2. The cat slept on the children's beds.

   The cat woke up.

   _____

3. We will stay in the park.

   We will leave for home.

   _____

4. In the morning Sam got ready for school.

   At night Sam did his homework.

   _____

5. There are too many books.

   I only have a few pieces of paper.

   _____

At Home: Help children list five pairs of antonyms. Encourage them to use two of the antonym pairs in sentences.

134

Book 2.2/Unit 1
Charlie Anderson   5

Soft *c* and Soft *g*

Write the word that answers the riddle.

1. This tells how old you are.

    lace   age   cage

_____

2. This is when you can run.

    page   ice   race

_____

3. This is something to eat.

    rice   rise   page

_____

4. This is something everyone has.

    lace   cage   face

_____

5. This is where a mouse might live.

    nice   cage   stage

_____

6. This is part of a book.

    page   place   dice

_____

7. This is what some tablecloths are made of.

    rice   page   lace

_____

8. This is what elephants are.

    cage   huge   race

_____

At Home: Have children list other words with **ce** and **ge.** Then have them use these words to make up one or two riddles of their own.

Vocabulary

Read the story. Choose a word from the box to complete each sentence. Write the word in the sentence. Then reread the story to check your answers.

diving	explains	harm	noisy	soil	village

The Browns go to a lake in the summer. They stay in

a house in the _____. Jess helps a baby bird.

His father _____ what happened. "This

morning the birds were very _____. A baby bird

came _____ out of its nest."

The bird lay in the dirt. It was covered with

_____. Jess is afraid a cat might _____

the little bird. He picks up the bird. Then he puts it on a

warm blanket. Later that day, the bird flies away.

The Noisy Village

I will tell you my idea," said George.

Good, thought Cindy, George explains things well.

"Every day we should have a two-hour quiet period," said George.

"Then people can take peaceful walks," added Cindy.

George's idea worked! Even the birds came back to the village.

At Home: Ask children to think of different ways to cut noise. Encourage them to try these things at home.

4

Long ago there was a village that
was so nice that more and more
people came.

People loved diving in the lake.
They planted trees and plants in the
rich soil. They laughed and played
games.

Finally, there were so many
people in the village that things
began to get noisy.

"It is so noisy I can't read a
page," said George.

"I haven't heard the birds since
last year!" said Cindy. "It is so noisy
they have gone away."

"This noise is going to harm us,"
said Lee. "What can we do?"

Story Comprehension

Think about "Fernando's Gift." Write the correct answer to complete each sentence.

1. Fernando lives in

_____ .

a. a rain forest

b. a city

2. Fernando's father plants

_____ .

a. rice

b. trees

3. The dogs are called

_____ .

a. Brown Dog and Black
Dog

b. Fido and Spot

4. Fernando's father also
teaches people about the

_____ .

a. dogs

b. rain forest

5. Carmina takes Fernando to

see her favorite _____

_____ .

a. river

b. climbing tree

6. The tree has _____

_____ .

a. been cut down

b. grown a lot

7. Fernando gives Carmina a

new _____ .

a. Cristobal tree

b. toy

8. They plant the tree in

_____ .

a. her yard

b. a secret place

At Home: Have children draw a picture of their
favorite part of the story. Then ask them to write a
sentence about it.

Read a Chart

The **chart** below gives weather facts for two cities in
Rhode Island. At a glance, you can compare the rainfall,
snowfall, and temperatures.

Month	Block Island Temperatures High	Low	Days of Rain or Snow	Providence Temperatures High	Low	Days of Rain or Snow
January	38	26	12	37	21	—
June	69	—	9	75	—	10
_____	70	57	8	72	53	8
November	51	39	—	51	34	10

Fill in the chart with the facts provided below. Use the
headings to guide you.

Facts to Add

- The low temperature in June in Providence was 56 degrees.

- There were 10 days of snow or rain in November on Block
  Island.

- In September, Block Island had a high temperature of 70 and
  a low of 57 degrees.

- There were 12 days of rain or snow in Providence in January.

- The low temperature on Block Island during June was 57
  degrees.

At Home: Help children to make a chart that shows
one of their activities over a week such as what they
138   ate, what they did, or when they went to bed.

Book 2.2/Unit 1
Fernando's Gift   5

Soft *c* and Soft *g*

Circle the word that completes each sentence. Then write it on the line.

I. Susan and Frannie are the same _____.

age   page   cage

2. I like to put _____ in a cold drink.

face   ice   lace

3. Sometimes we have _____ for dinner.

lace   twice   rice

4. My mouse lives in a _____.

page   cage   age

5. Stephan ran fast and won the _____.

race   face   rice

6. Jake forgot which _____ he was reading.

stage   age   page

6   Book 2.2/Unit 1
Fernando's Gift

At Home: Have children write the words they circled in alphabetical order.

139

Soft *c, g;* /ŭ/*oo*

Write a word from the box to complete each sentence.

book	mice	looked	face	place
stage	slice	page	nice	twice

1. I am reading a _____ on cooking.

2. The baby has a smile on her _____.

3. I visited the _____ where grandma grew up.

4. There are _____ in the field.

5. Actors do shows on a _____.

6. We stopped the car and _____ at the view.

7. We played the game _____.

8. My mother cut me a _____ of cake.

9. A kind person is _____.

10. Turn the _____ of the book.

At Home: Have children make up a rhyme for the word wood.

Book 2.2/Unit 1
Fernando's Gift
10

Compare and Contrast

Imagine that you are a new student. At first you do not have any friends. Soon, you and Pat become good friends.

Write a letter to an old friend. Write about how you felt when you first came to the new school. Then write about how you felt after you got to know Pat.

Dear _____,

   I have been at my new school for two weeks.

At first, I felt _____. When we went out to

play, I _____.

After I met Pat, I felt _____.

Now when I go out to play, _____.

                              Your friend,

                        _____

At Home: Have children compare and contrast their feelings about a current event at school, such as the arrival or departure of a class pet.

Antonyms

Two words that are opposite in meaning are called
antonyms.

Mia got **wet** in the rain.
She sat by the heater until she was **dry**.

Wet and **dry** are antonyms. They are opposite in meaning.

Read each pair of sentences. Look at the underlined word
in the first sentence. Then complete the second sentence
in each pair with an antonym for the underlined word.

1. It was <u>noisy</u> at the baseball game.

   It was _____ in the library.

2. There are <u>few</u> cars in the village.

   There are _____ cars in the city.

3. Because it is so <u>hot</u> we go swimming.

   We wear heavy clothes on _____ days.

4. The <u>tall</u> man could reach the shelf.

   The _____ man stood on a chair to reach the shelf.

5. Yesterday morning the ocean was <u>calm</u>.

   The ocean was very _____ during the storm.

At Home: Encourage children to write three original
sentences. Then have them substitute an antonym for
one of the words in each sentence.

142

Book 2.2/Unit 1
Fernando's Gift

5

/ô/ a, aw, au

taught	claw	saw	caught	lawn	hawk

Write the word that names the picture and answers the riddle.

1.

   A crab has two of these.

   claws   paws   saws

2.

   This is a kind of bird.

   fawn   hawk   bat

3.

   Your teacher did this last week.

   cooked   taught   painted

4.

   This is what people mow.

   lawn   dawn   saw

5.

   This cuts wood.

   paw   claw   saw

5

Book 2.2/Unit 1
The Best Vacation Ever

At Home: Have children make up a riddle for each word in the box.

143

Vocabulary

Read each sentence. Write **T** if the sentence is true.
Write **F** if the sentence is false. In each sentence,
underline a word from the word box.

| brave | guess | museum | practice | vacation | wonder |

_____ 1. A brave person is always afraid.

_____ 2. If you don't know something, you can guess.

_____ 3. When you practice music, you forget how to play.

_____ 4. An art museum is a place to see paintings.

_____ 5. A vacation is a time when you don't have school.

_____ 6. If you wonder about something, you know about it.

_____ 7. Most people don't like to take a vacation.

_____ 8. You can go swimming at a museum.

_____ 9. A brave girl will do something she is afraid of.

_____ 10. You can practice something to learn how to do it.

_____ 11. When you guess, you know for sure.

_____ 12. You might wonder which foods are best for you.

144

At Home: Have children write sentences to correct the
false statements.

Book 2.2/Unit 1
The Best Vacation Ever
12

Train Travel

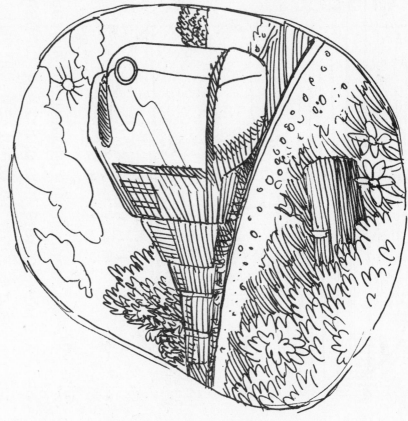

station. But we had to go back to the hotel. I had forgotten my suitcase. My father just smiled. I wonder what he was thinking.

Mom was happy to see us when we got home. My father said that we had taken the trip of our lives!

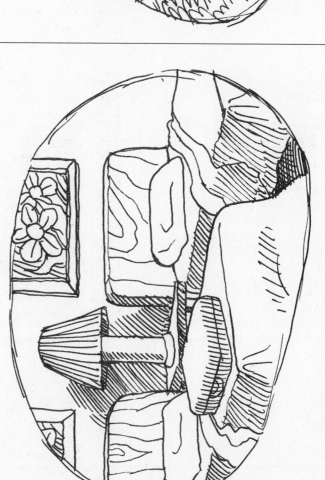

At Home: Talk with children about interesting places they have been or would like to visit. Ask them what makes these places interesting.

4

My dad is a very brave man. He took my brother and me away on vacation without my mother. She had to work.

We went to the city by train. My brother and I never saw a large city before.

The first day there we went to the museum. We could only stay a short time. My brother got the hiccups.

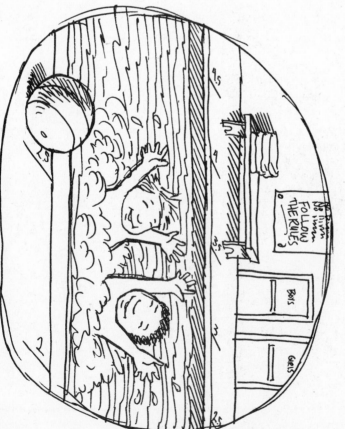

The next day, to went swimming. My father taught us to practice for a swim contest. We only stayed a little while. I started to sneeze!

The day after that my father woke up early. "Guess what we are going to do today?" he asked.

"I don't know," I answered.

"We're going home," my father said. "Mom misses the two of you."

Story Comprehension

Read each sentence. Write **T** if the sentence is true.
Write **F** if the sentence if false.

1. _____ Amanda drove across the country with her family.

2. _____ They saw where Orville Wright flew the first plane.

3. _____ The home of country music is in Kitty Hawk.

4. _____ The Grand Ole Opry is a place to hear country music.

5. _____ The Alamo is in Texas.

6. _____ Amanda said, "Carlsbad Caverns were not very big."

7. _____ Amanda and her family rode mules in the Grand Canyon.

8. _____ Sammy liked riding a mule.

9. _____ After the Grand Canyon, Amanda went home.

10. _____ There are millions of bones in the La Brea Tarpits.

10 Book 2.2/ Unit 1
The Best Vacation Ever

At Home: Have children tell about one of the places
that Amanda visited with her family.

145

Read a Map

Pretend you want to take a trip to the Southwest. You will want to visit some special sites your friends have told you about. Use the **map** below to plan your trip. Write the answer on the blank space beside the questions.

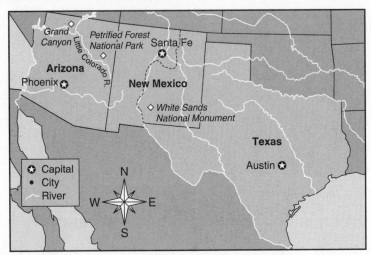

1. You will start your visit in Phoenix, Arizona. You want to visit the Grand Canyon first. Which direction will you have to go to get there? _____

2. Your next stop will be the Petrified Forest National Park. What river is that near? _____

3. What is the capital of New Mexico? _____

4. From Santa Fe, you want to go to the White Sands National Monument. In which direction would you go?

_____

At Home: Help children to identify the direction (north, south, east or west) you'd have to travel to reach a local landmark.

146

Book 2.2/Unit 1
The Best Vacation Ever

4

/ô/ a, aw, au

A. Circle the word to complete each sentence. Then write it on the line.

1. The crab grabs with its _____.

   hawk   claw   paw

2. I _____ when I get tired.

   lawn   paw   yawn

3. The _____ has many white spots.

   fawn   draw   law

B. Circle the word to complete each sentence. Then write it on the line.

4. We moved to a bigger house _____ we had a new baby.

   because   taught   caught

5. The teacher _____ math yesterday.

   taught   caught   because

6. Billy _____ the ball and the game was over.

   taught   because   caught

/ô/ a, aw, au; Soft c, g; /ủ/

Use these words to answer the riddles.

hawk	age	hood	astronaut	foot	ice

I. I fly in a spaceship. What am I?

_____

2. I am very cold. What am I?

_____

3. I am a kind of bird. What am I?

_____

4. I am another word for how old you are. What am I?

_____

5. People use me when they walk. What am I?

_____

6. I am part of your coat. I keep your head warm. What am I?

_____

At Home: Have children make up a riddle for the word book.

Draw Conclusions

Read the story. Write the answer to each question.
Use a complete sentence.

Jamie loves to do magic tricks. She wants to buy the magic kit in Mr. Britt's store. First she has to save enough money from her weekly allowance. Every day Jamie walks by the store to make sure the kit is in the window. Mr. Britt told her he would save one for her. Many weeks later, Jamie finally has enough money. When she gets to the store, the kit is gone from the window!

1. Do you think that the magic kit costs a little bit of money or a lot of money?

_____

2. What makes you think this?

_____

3. How do you think Jamie felt when she didn't see the magic kit?

_____

_____

4. Do you think Jamie finally got the magic kit? Why?

_____

_____

_____

At Home: Have children change some of the information in the story. Ask them how this would change the conclusions they first made.

Inflectional Endings

The **-er** ending is used to compare two people, places, or things.
fast + **er** = faster (more fast)
Sam runs **faster** than Mike runs.

The **-est** ending is used to compare more than two people, places or things.
tall + **est** = tallest (most tall)
That is the **tallest** building in the state.

Complete the sentences with the correct words.

1. Winter will be here soon. It is only six o'clock, yet the sky is
_____ (darker, darkest) than it was a week ago. In fact,
this is the _____ (cooler, coolest) day in over a week.
Soon the days will be _____ (shorter, shortest) than the
nights. The fireplace is the _____ (warmer, warmest)
spot in the house.

2. We are proud of the library in our community. The building is
_____ (newer, newest) than the library on Main Street.
There are many books to read in the Children's Room. In fact,
that is the _____ (busier, busiest) reading room in the
whole library.

At Home: Have children add **-er** and **-est** to the ends of the following words: **small, slow, new,** and **great.** Then ask the children to use each word in an original sentence that compares two or more people, places, or things.

Book 2.2/Unit 1
The Best Vacation Ever
6

Digraphs *ph, tch*

Read the words. Then, in each row, circle the pictures for the words that contain **ph** or **tch**.

1. ca*tch*

2. *ph*oto

3. pi*tch*er

4. gra*ph*

6 | Book 2.2/Unit 1
Zipping, Zapping, Zooming Bats

At Home: Have children draw a picture that includes at least four of the items circled on this page.

151

Vocabulary

Read the words in the box. Read the clues. Write the correct word on the line next to each clue.

disturb	**explore**	**facts**	**nature**	**objects**	**several**

1. This word means more than two.

_____

2. These are things that you know are true.

_____

3. You can do this to a baby by being noisy.

_____

4. These are things that you can see or touch.

_____

5. You could do this on the moon.

_____

6. Plants and animals are part of this.

_____

152

At Home: Have your child make up riddles for some of the words in the box.

Book 2.2/Unit 1
Zipping, Zapping, Zooming Bats 6

Desert Friends

Welcome, the man said. Sit
down and I will tell you many facts
about the desert. This place is a real
nature center. See the mountains in
the distance? There are great forests
on the other side of them."

"I used to live in a forest," said
Phil. "Would you like a sandwich?"

"That would be nice," said the old
man. And the three became friends.

At Home: Have children write about things they have
seen or would like to see on a nature trip.

One day Phil and his dad left home to explore the desert. They packed water, several sandwiches, and a tent to pitch on their trip.

As they walked, Phil watched many animals and objects he had never seen before. There were plants and rocks. There were birds, lizards, and mice he wanted to photograph.

Zipping, Zapping, Zooming Bats McGraw-Hill School Division

Phil and his dad saw a small house in the distance. As they walked closer they saw a sign on the door that read, "Do Not Disturb!"

"I wonder who lives there?" Phil thought.

Suddenly an old man on crutches stepped out from the house. "Who are you?" he shouted.

"I am Phil. This is my dad. We are exploring the desert."

Story Comprehension

Think about "Zipping, Zapping, Zooming Bats."
Finish each sentence by underlining the answer.

1. Bats come out to hunt
_____ .

   a. when the sun goes down

   b. in the daytime

2. Bats eat lots of _____ .

   a. peanut butter

   b. insects

3. Bats use _____ to help them hunt.

   a. their eyes

   b. sounds

4. When bats sleep, they _____ .

   a. hang upside down

   b. keep their eyes open

5. Bats _____ with their tongues and claws.

   a. clean themselves

   b. hunt in the daytime

6. Many bats _____ during winter.

   a. move

   b. sleep

7. Bats are the only flying
_____ .

   a. mammals

   b. birds

8. Some kinds of bats are
_____ .

   a. living at the North Pole

   b. in danger of dying out

8   Book 2.2/Unit 1
Zipping, Zapping, Zooming Bats

At Home: Have children write about one or two things they learned from the story.

153

Read a map

 fish

 whale

 island

 ferry

 rocks

 harbor

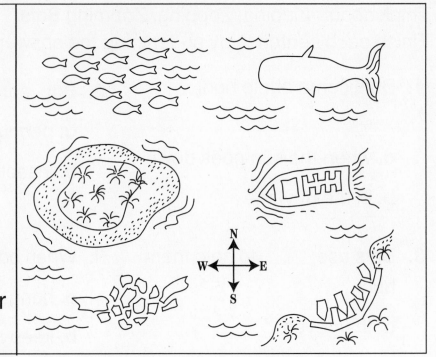

Use this map to finish each sentence. Circle the answer.

1. _____ shows where there are fish.

2. _____ shows where there are rocks.

3. The whale is ___ of the harbor.

south   north   east

4. The island is ___ of the ferry.

west   east   south

5. The ferry is east of the ___.

harbor   whale   island

6. The fish must swim ___ to get to the rocks.

west   south   north

At Home: Ask the children to identify all the rivers that they see on this map (Mississippi, Ohio, Arkansas and Missouri rivers).

154

Book 2.2/ unit 1
Zipping, Zapping, Zooming Bats

6

Digraphs *ph, tch*

Circle the word that describes each sentence.
Then write the word.

1. A door has one of these.

latch   catch   stitch

_____

2. You can light a fire with this.

match   photo   itch

_____

3. This can ring anytime.

photograph phone stretch

_____

4. This can make you taller.

graph   patch   stretch

_____

5. This is a person who takes pictures.

photographer doctor photo

_____

6. You can tell time with this.

patch   hatch   watch

_____

7. This is what a bat does to an insect.

catch   itch   phone

_____

8. This is when you throw a ball to a batter.

graph   pitch   match

_____

8   Book 2.2/Unit 1
Zipping, Zapping, Zooming Bats

At Home: Have children use four of the words they wrote in a sentence.

155

tch; /ô/; Soft c, g

Choose the word that completes the sentence. Write the word.

draw	page	pace	tossed	rice
catch	author	fall	switch	bought

1. The dog can _____ the ball in its mouth.

2. I will _____ a picture of a boat with a crayon.

3. My father made white _____ and beans.

4. It is cold outside, so we walk at a fast _____.

5. I turned to the next _____ in my book.

6. Jane and Pilar _____ the ball back and forth.

7. The _____ is the person who writes the book.

8. It will be dark after you flip the light _____ to "off."

9. Be careful not to slip and _____ on the ice.

10. I _____ food at the store.

At Home: Have children write new sentences for the words above.

Compare and Contrast

When you **compare**, you tell how things are alike.
When you **contrast**, you tell how things are different.

Make two lists. Write three sentences that explain ways in which bats are alike. Write three sentences that explain ways in which bats are different.

ALIKE:

1. _____

2. _____

_____

3. _____

_____

_____

DIFFERENT:

4. _____

_____

5. _____

_____

6. _____

_____

6 Book 2.2/Unit 1
Zipping, Zapping, Zooming Bats

At Home: Have children draw a picture of a bat. Then have them write down some of the things they remember about bats.

157

Inflectional Endings

You can use words such as **brighter** and **widest** to make comparisons.

The sun looks **brighter** than Earth.

That river is the **longest** of all the rivers in the state.

Add **-er** or **-est** to one of the words in the box to complete each sentence.

tall	green	long	warm	fast	fresh

1. Because Ted ran _____ than Jim, he won the race.

2. Now I am two inches _____ than my sister.

3. This is the _____ weather we have had all summer.

4. This story about bats is the _____ one in the book.

5. This bread, which was just baked, is _____ than the bread on the table.

6. The grass is _____ this spring than it was last spring.

At Home: Ask children to make up original sentences using the following words: **smaller, smallest, larger, largest, darker,** and **darkest.**

Book 2.2/Unit 1
Zipping, Zapping, Zooming Bats
6

ph, tch; /ô/; Soft *c, g; /ù/*

Circle the word that answers the riddle. Then write the word.

1. This is a very, very big animal.

mouse   elephant   skunk

_____

2. This is never bad.

good   watch   phone

_____

3. This is good to drink.

saw   juice   rice

_____

4. This could go over a river.

cage   age   bridge

_____

5. This is what my teacher did all year.

caught   taught   laugh

_____

6. This is very cold.

ice   face   race

_____

7. This will tell you the time.

stretch   itch   watch

_____

8. This will cut wood.

saw   paw   aunt

_____

8 Book 2.2/Unit 1
Going Batty for Bats

At Home: Have children make up another riddle for each of the words they circled.

159

Vocabulary

Read the story. Choose a word from the box to complete each sentence. Write the word in the sentence. Then reread the story to check your answers.

breath	cover	crops	darkness	scary	study

Today is Sunday. It is very cold today. I can even

see my _____ in the air. Out in the fields, all the

_____ have ice on them. Thick fog _____

them too.

Finally, I came inside to _____ for a test. It

is getting late. I can see that _____ is coming.

It seems _____ out there in the dark. I am safe

and warm in my house. My mom brings me a glass of

apple juice.

At Home: Have children use words from the box to write two more sentences to tell what might have happened next.

The Bat Cave

That took my breath away," said
Mrs. Bat as they dove down by a rock.

"Let me go study that rock," said
Mr. Bat. He flew down low, then
came back. "I found a giant place.
It's a cave!"

"Perfect!" said Mrs. Bat. And they
flew to their new home, filled with
plenty of cozy darkness.

At Home: Help children write a 3–5-line summary of the story.

4

"We need a new place to live,"
said Mrs. Bat.

"Yes," said Mr. Bat. "With Baby
Bat we will need more room."

First they looked in a phone booth.
"Too small," said Mrs. Bat.

They flew high over a village.
"Too many people," said Mrs. Bat.
"They are much too scary."

As they flew they watched people
working in fields.
"Those are rice crops," said Mr.
Bat.

"Fly on," said Mrs. Bat.

Baby Bat was getting tired. He let
out a high-pitched yell.

Just then a mean looking hawk
flew by.
"Take cover!" said Mr. Bat.

Story Comprehension

Think about "Going Batty for Bats." Answer each question. Write complete sentences.

1. How do bats help people?

_____

_____

2. How can people help bats?

_____

_____

3. What city has the largest bat colony in the United States?

_____

_____

4. What is the scariest thing about a bat?

_____

_____

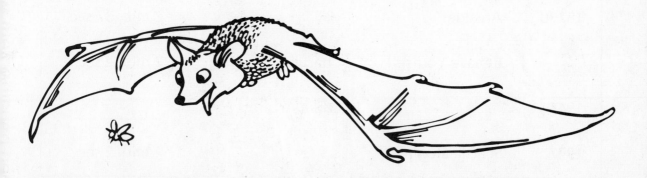

4 Book 2.2/Unit 1
Going Batty for Bats

At Home: Have children tell what they would do if they found a bat in their house.

161

Use a Chart

It is often easier to read facts in a **chart** than in a paragraph. Read the paragraph below. Notice how the facts tend to get confusing.

> The Kentucky Derby is one of the most famous races in the world. On the first Saturday in May, horses race over one and a quarter miles. The first Kentucky Derby took place in 1875. The winner was a horse called Aristides. It took Aristides two minutes and thirty-seven seconds to finish the course. The jockey was Oliver Lewis. In 1921, a horse called Behave Yourself won the race in two minutes and four seconds. The jockey was Charles Thompson. One of the most famous horses, Whirlaway, was ridden by Eddie Arcaro. In 1941, he won in two minutes, one second. Another famous horse, Seattle Slew, won in 1977, finishing in two minutes and two seconds. The jockey was Jean Cruguet.

Fill in the blanks using the information in the paragraph.

Kentucky Derby Results			
Year	Winner	Jockey	Time
1875	Aristides	_____	2 min. 37 sec.
____	Behave Yourself	Charles Thompson	2 min. 4 sec.
1941	_____	Eddie Arcaro	_____
1977	Seattle Slew	_____	2 min. 2 sec.

At Home: Show children other examples of charts from newspapers and magazines.

162

Book 2.2/Unit 1
Going Batty for Bats

5

Compare and Contrast

When you **compare**, you tell how things are alike.
When you **contrast**, you tell how things are different.

Some people are afraid of bats. Help them learn not to be scared. For each statement, write something different that you learned in "Going Batty for Bats."

1. Bats hurt people.

_____

2. Bats eat farm crops.

_____

3. Bats don't eat very much.

_____

4. Putting a gate on a cave hurts bats.

_____

5. You should be scared if you see a bat.

_____

5 Book 2.2/Unit 1
Going Batty for Bats

At Home: Have children think of different places that might make a good home for a bat.

163

Draw Conclusions

Read the clues. Write what you think the clues mean under the word **conclusion**.

Clue	Clue	Conclusion
1. Tia sees a black and white animal.	It squirts something very smelly.	_____ _____

Clue	Clue	Conclusion
2. Kate can see over a high fence.	Her pants are always too short.	_____ _____

Clue	Clue	Conclusion
3. Buck never puts his toys away.	His bed is not made.	_____ _____

Clue	Clue	Conclusion
4. Mom has worked hard all day.	Mom is yawning.	_____ _____

At Home: Have children make up clues about a story character. Have classmates guess who the story character is.

164

Book 2.2/Unit 1
Going Batty for Bats

4

Inflectional Endings

Add **-er** to the ends of words to compare two people, places, or things.
Tim is **older** (more old) than Megan.

Add **-est** to the ends of words to compare more than two people, places, or things.
Ryan is the **oldest** (most old) student in our class.

Read each sentence. Then add **-er** or **-est** to the word in dark print. Write the word on the line.

1. Lee's bike is **new** than my bike.

_____

2. That red bird flew the **fast**.

_____

3. We will cut down the **large** tree in the forest.

_____

4. There are **few** flowers in the garden this year than there were last year.

_____

5. That lamp is the **bright** one in the store.

_____

6. Pam feels much **strong** than she did last week.

_____

At Home: Have children add **-er** and **-est** to the following words: **fresh, dark,** and **warm.** Then have them use each word in a sentence.

Antonyms

Two words that are opposite or almost opposite in meaning are **antonyms**.

Read each sentence. Choose an antonym for the word in dark print from the box below. Write the antonym on the line.

catch	winter	bottom	night	weak	stop

1. I will **start** the race.

_____

2. We will leave food for the birds in the **morning**.

_____

3. Be careful not to **throw** the ball into Mr. Morgan's backyard.

_____

4. We will visit our grandparents' farm this **summer**.

_____

5. No one in the village was **strong** enough to push the rock.

_____

6. The students put their book reports on **top** of the table.

_____

At Home: Help children identify an antonym for each of these words: **light, long, old, late.** Have them use three of the antonym pairs in new sentences.

166

Book 2.2/Unit 1
Going Batty for Bats

6

Unit 1 Vocabulary Review

A. Use the words in the box to complete the story.

| museum   chocolate   explore   vacation   nature   village |

I live in a small _____ called Hamilton.

We have a library, a _____, and a store that

sells _____- chip cookies. Many people

come to Hamilton for their summer _____.

They like to _____ the forest. They also go

to the _____ center to learn about plants .

B. Draw a line to the word or words that mean the
opposite. Then, write this answer on the line.

_____ **1.** upstairs   quiet

_____ **2.** harm   cowardly

_____ **3.** darkness   downstairs

_____ **4.** noisy   help

_____ **5.** brave   leave alone

_____ **6.** disturb   light

At Home: Have children think of words that mean
almost the same thing as the words in Exercise B.

Unit 1 Vocabulary Review

A. Write a question for each statement below. Use the underlined word in your question.

I ate some chocolate cake.
How much chocolate cake did you eat?

---

1. I bought new clothes. _____

2. I study every night. _____

3. She is diving into the pool. _____

4. I tried to guess the right answer. _____

_____

5. I practice the piano every day. _____

B. Answer **Yes** or **No** to the questions below, and explain your answers.

1. If a friend offered her help building a model airplane, would

   you take it? _____

2. Is a roof the same thing as a floor? _____

_____

3. Do you ever wear anything to cover your head? _____

_____

At Home: Have children write three questions using
vocabulary words from Part A.

Book 2.2/Unit 1
Unit 1 Vocabulary Review   8

/âr/ *are*; /ôr/ *or, ore*; /îr/ *ear*

Write a word from the box to complete each sentence.

careful   scared   story   for   stored   morning   more   hear

1. Kitty waited _____ Sally.

2. The loud noise _____ us.

3. Mom reads me a _____ every night.

4. I am _____ when I ride my bike.

5. We eat breakfast every _____.

6. I'm cold, so put on _____ heat.

7. Luis wanted to _____ the song.

8. The clothes are _____ in the closet.

8 Book 2.2/ Unit 2
The Bremen Town Musicians

At Home: Invite children to write a story using words from the box.

169

Vocabulary

| scare | third | daughter | music | voice | whistle |

Read each sentence. Choose a word from the box that means almost the same thing as the words in dark type. Write it on the line.

1. They took their (**girl child**) to the movies. _____

2. Alex can (**make a sound with his lips**). _____

3. John lost his key for the (**three in a row**) time. _____

4. The children (**make people afraid**) with their masks. _____

5. I love to play (**nice sounds**) on the guitar. _____

6. Luke has a strong speaking (**sound from his mouth**). _____

170

At Home: Have children make up questions using three of the vocabulary words.

Book 2.2/Unit 2
The Bremen Town Musicians
6

Lina Saves the Play

she said her lines. But Sandy did not turn on the music, and José did not wake Maria. Luckily, Lina whistled the song and woke the daughter.

Everyone yelled, "More! More!"

"You saved the day, Lina," said Mrs. Rose.

4

At Home: Have children write about a time they were scared, and what they did to get through their fear.

Mrs. Rose's class was putting on the third play of the school year.

"The play is about a queen's daughter," said Mrs. Rose. "She is put under a spell and falls asleep."

"I want to be the daughter," said Lina.

"No," said Mrs. Rose. "You have a nice voice. You will be the storyteller. She talks clearly through the whole play so people can hear."

The Bremen Town Musicians McGraw-Hill School Division

"Yes," said Mrs. Rose. "You tell the story. Sandy will take care of the music. José will wake the daughter. And Maria will play the daughter."

I am glad I got the part of the daughter, Maria thought. If I had to talk, it would scare me.

Story Comprehension

Think about what happened in "The Bremen Town Musicians." Then answer the questions.

1. Why did the donkey run away?

   _____

2. Why did the dog run away?

   _____

3. Why did the cat run away?

   _____

4. Why did the rooster run away?

   _____

5. Where did the animals go?

   _____

6. Why did the robbers run away?

   _____

6 Book 2.2/Unit 2
The Bremen Town Musicians

At Home: Invite children to tell what happened next in the story.

171

Follow Directions

Learning a task is easier when it's divided into parts.
Below is a list of **directions** you follow when you are
brushing your teeth. Rewrite the directions in the proper
order so that they make sense.

Rinse your mouth.
Find your toothbrush and your tube of toothpaste.
Dry your face.
Put your toothbrush and tube of toothpaste away.
Put toothpaste on the toothbrush.
Brush your teeth.

1. _____

2. _____

3. _____

4. _____

5. _____

6. _____

At Home: Help children to write the directions for a
simple receipe.

172

Book 2.2/Unit 2
The Bremen Town Musicians

6

/âr/ *are*; /ôr/ *or, ore*; /îr/ *ear*

Complete the words by writing in the correct letters. Then
write the full word after the sentence.

are	or	ore	ear

1. The letter began, "D_____ Linda." _____

2. Baseball and football are great sp_____ts. _____

3. Don't be sc_____d. It is safe here. _____

4. We buy milk at the st_____e. _____

5. The rooster crows in the m_____ning. _____

6. After the rain, the sky was cl_____. _____

7. It is good to sh_____ with others. _____

8. Please open the door f_____ me. _____

[8] Book 2.2/ Unit 2
The Bremen Town Musicians

At Home: Have children recite each of the words on
this page.

173

/âr/ are; /ôr/ or, ore; /îr/ ear

Write the word from the box that completes each
sentence.

tears	care	thorns	share	more
storm	sore	scare	store	clear

1. That was tasty! Can I have some _____?

2. Wipe those _____ from your eyes.

3. Some bushes have sharp _____.

4. Tina and Toni like to _____ their toys.

5. A tree fell during the _____.

6. I _____ about all animals.

7. My legs are _____ from running.

8. Go to the _____ and buy a pencil.

9. I don't see any clouds; the sky is blue and _____.

10. Don't yell. You will _____ the baby.

At Home: Have children write a story using the words
in the box above.

Summarize

Read each story. Then put a line under the best summary.

1. Jay has a blue bird. Min has a black bird. Mary has two white birds.

   a. The birds like the children.
   b. All the children have birds.
   c. Birds make good pets.

2. We saw a black animal with white stripes. As we got closer, we saw that it was starting to get angry. We left it alone!

   a. We saw a skunk.
   b. We got angry.
   c. We left the black animal.

3. Jake puts the towels and beach balls in the car. Then his dad packs the lunches. Jake can't wait to jump in the waves!

   a. Jake and his dad eat lunch.
   b. Jake's family goes to the beach.
   c. Jake throws beach balls.

4. I draw animals all the time. I also like to draw people. Sometimes I like to draw people while they work.

   a. I only draw people.
   b. I draw animals well.
   c. I like to draw.

5. We unpacked the boxes. We hung our pictures, and we moved our furniture. Now we are home!

   a. We moved the pictures.
   b. We bought new furniture.
   c. We moved into a new home.

Suffixes

You can add **-ful** and **-ly** to some words to make new words.

thank + **-ful** = thankful   quick + **-ly** = quickly

Thankful means "full of thanks." Quickly means "in a quick way."

Read each sentence. Write a word with **-ful** or **-ly** that means the same as the underlined words in each sentence.

1. My mom drives in a slow way past the school. _____

2. Please be full of care when you cross the street. _____

3. The circus tent was full of color. _____

4. The storm came in a sudden way from the west. _____

5. We are full of hope that the rain will stop soon. _____

6. Lulu tiptoed in a quiet way past the baby. _____

7. My little brother smiled in a shy way. _____

8. Everyone at the party was full of joy. _____

At Home: Ask children to add **-ly** or **-ful** to these words to make new words: **eager, glad, firm, fear.**

/ü/ *oo, ue, ew*

Circle the word that fits in the sentence. Then write the word.

1. I wear a _____ on one

   foot.

   boot   beet   boat

2. A _____ is a loud sound.

   broom   boom   bone

3. The sky is _____

   blew   blue   blow

4. The bird _____ away.

   few   flaw   flew

5. Joe wants to come, _____.

   toe   tow   too

6. Last night, the wind

   _____ hard.

   blue   blew   blow

7. _____ the broken

   vase back together.

   Clue   Glue   Blew

8. We eat at _____

   every day.

   noon   tune   soon

8 Book 2.2/Unit 2
Our Soccer League

At Home: Ask children to think of a riddle or a rhyme
using **oo, ue,** or **ew** words.

177

Vocabulary

Circle the word that answers the riddle. Then write the word on the line.

coaches	field	score	stretches	throws	touch

1. These are good to do before you play sports. _____

field   stretches   objects

2. This is what David does with a ball. _____

throws   whistles   scares

3. You can do this to a table, a book, or a chair. _____

sleep   score   touch

4. We are the people who run the team. _____

coaches   police   nurses

5. This is what happens when a ball goes in the goal. _____

safe   score   wild

6. I am the place where ball games are played. _____

house   barn   field

At Home: Have children make up riddles using some of the words that they didn't circle.

The Blue
Birds

"Now we are going to lose big time!" I say.

"That's not true! Wait and see," says Martha.

Boom! Ted hits the ball! Then Joe hits the ball! Then I hit a home run, too! We win!

"You see," says Martha. "I knew you were a good team all along. You just had to believe in yourselves!"

At Home: Have children draw a picture and write a few sentences about their favorite sport. Who is their favorite player. Why?

4

178a

2

The Blue Birds! What an awful baseball team! Every time we get on the field we lose. We never touch base or score.

The coaches try to be nice. "You will do better next time," say Mr. Rivera and Mrs. Nelson.

We know better, though. We do not do our stretches. We do not want to practice. We are losers.

Our Soccer League McGraw-Hill School Division

Then one day a new girl named Martha comes to play. She is a great hitter. She throws the ball really far.

Suddenly, we are not losers anymore. We do our stretches. We start to hit better.

Everything is going very well until Martha hurts her hand. It happens right before the playoffs.

3

178b

Story Comprehension

Think about the story "Our Soccer League." Draw pictures
to show six things you learned about soccer. Write a label
for each picture.

1. _____	2. _____
3. _____	4. _____
5. _____	6. _____

At Home: Have children pretend to be sports
announcers, announcing the players and moves in
a soccer game.

Read a Newsletter

Different **newsletters** are aimed at different readers.

Newsletter #1

CHESS CLUB NEWS
by Peter Kingsley

The final match of the chess tournament was played Tuesday after school. Tanya Quigly went head to head with Victor Sing. The winner was the first to gain three points. A win was worth one point. A draw was worth a half point. Victor won the first match. Tanya pulled out a tie in the second. And then Tanya got a check-mate in sixteen moves in the third. But Victor won two straight games. They were both close but Victor is our new champion!

Newsletter #2

GABRIEL STREET BLOCK ASSOCIATION NEWSLETTER

Block clean-up Saturday! All day!
Be there or be square! Bring a friend!
Take pride in our block. The city is sending a special garbage truck just for us. The vacant lot will be cleared. Trees will be planted. Bus benches will be painted. Gabby's Deli is bringing sandwiches. If you have anything to bring to the block yard sale, call Tom 555-2345. A clean block is a happy block!!

Use the information in the two newsletters above to answer the questions that follow.

1. Which newsletter was written for the people who lived in a

   certain area? _____

2. Which newsletter told who wrote it? _____

3. Who won the final match of the chess club? _____

4. When is the big block clean up? _____

5. What is the main idea of each newsletter?

   _____

   _____

At Home: Have children write newsletters about their lives to send to family and friends.

/ü/ oo, ue, ew

The answer to each riddle has the same ending sound as cl**ue**, st**ew**, or t**oo**. Circle the word. Write each answer on the line.

1. What does a
ghost say?

boo
boom
bow

_____

2. What do you
do with food?

clue
chew
bow

_____

3. What did the
flower do?

gray
grew
good

_____

4. What is the
name of a color

blew
buy
blue

_____

5. What does a
cow say?

boom
moo
too

_____

6. What is
sticky?

glue
grow
glow

_____

7. Which word
means **also**?

too
room
to

_____

8. Which word
means **not old**?

no
now
new

_____

8

Book 2.2/Unit 2
Our Soccer League

At Home: Help children use the words they wrote in a sentence.

181

/ü/ *oo, ue;* /ôr/ *or, ore*

Underline the word that completes the sentence. Then write the answer.

1. Fish is my favorite _____.

   food   boot   hoot

2. The _____ of the soccer game is tied.

   score   tore   store

3. The sky is _____ today.

   clue   blue   true

4. I wake up in the _____.

   born   morning   worn

5. We needed _____ for our art project.

   blue   true   glue

6. My sister plays the _____.

   core   short   horn

At Home: Have children illustrate one of the sentences
182 above.

Book 2.2/Unit 2
Our Soccer League
6

Sequence of Events

Read the story. Then write first, next, then, and last below the sentence to show when Lisa did each thing.

Teams	1st half	2nd half	Final
Tigers	3	2	5
Cubs	2	0	2

Lisa keeps score for the Tigers. Today they are playing the Cubs. In the first half, the Tigers scored 3 goals. The Cubs scored 2 goals. The Tigers played hard during the second half. Jeff scored a goal. Meg kicked a goal, too. Lisa put a 2 on the scoreboard. The whistle blew. The game was over. Lisa counted up the goals. She put the number in the last box. The Tigers won!

Lisa wrote a 5 in the box.

_____

Lisa gave the Tigers a 3

_____

Lisa gave the Cubs a 2.

_____

The Cubs scored 0 and the Tigers scored 2.

_____

4 Book 2.2/Unit 2
Our Soccer League

At Home: Have children tell about common events or activities that involve a sequence, for example, getting dressed or planting a seed.

183

Context Clues

Read each sentence. You can find clues about the meaning of the underlined word by reading the rest of the sentence. Color in the circle next to the word's definition.

1. In this game you throw a ball through a <u>basket</u>.

   ⓐ an open net on a metal ring

   ⓑ a swimming pool

2. At <u>halftime</u>, we take a break.

   ⓐ a young player

   ⓑ when the game is half over

3. The <u>score</u> is ten to twelve.

   ⓐ the number of points made in a game

   ⓑ a very big number

4. The <u>coach</u> helps us learn to throw.

   ⓐ a special throw

   ⓑ a teacher in sports

5. The players <u>charge</u> down the court.

   ⓐ pay for with a credit card

   ⓑ run fast

At Home: Read a picture caption from the sports section of your newspaper and help your child learn new words by using clues given in words and pictures.

184

Book 2.2/Unit 2
Our Soccer League
5

/ər/ *er;* /ən/ *en;* /əl/ *le*

Write the word from the box that completes each sentence.

dinner	candle	wiggle	handle
oven	water	happen	mother

1. We had soup for _____.

2. We put one red _____ on Billy's cake.

3. Be careful! The _____ is hot.

4. The coat belonged to my _____.

5. Dad washed the dishes in warm _____.

6. I can _____ like a snake.

7. Anything can _____!

8. The _____ to the teapot broke.

8 | Book 2.2/Unit 2
The Wednesday Surprise

At Home: Ask children to suggest a rhyming word for
one of the words they wrote.

185

Vocabulary

Write the words from the box to finish the letter.

chance favorite heavy nervous office wrapped

Dear Pete,

I'm sitting in my dad's _____. He is talking on

the phone. I want to tell you about the present I just got.

It was _____ in red paper. I hoped it was my

_____ book about bears. I thought there was a

_____ that it was. When I picked it up, it was

_____. I was _____ when I opened it.

Guess what! It wasn't the book about bears. It was a

book about the sky! You'll have to see it when you visit.

Your friend,

Doug

At Home: Have children write a new sentence for each of the words.

186

Book 2.2/Unit 2
The Wednesday Surprise
6

MOM'S SECRET

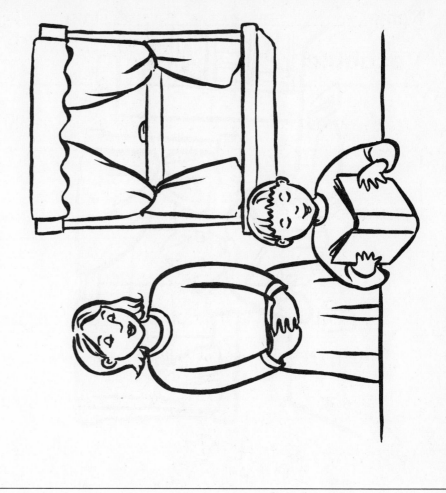

How did that happen?" I asked.

"When I came to this country I did not know English. I can speak it now. But I never had the chance to learn how to read it."

"I will help you learn now," I said. And together we sat down to read a book.

At Home: Discuss with children the importance of reading. Why is it important to read? What are some of the children's favorite books?

4

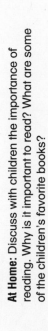

186a

It all began when I was seven. I was at the dinner table reading a heavy book.

"Put the book away," Mom said.

"But it is my favorite book," I said. "Would you like to see it?"

"It is time for dinner now," she said.

The Wednesday Surprise McGraw-Hill School Division

After dinner I talked to Dad in his office. I showed Dad my book. "Mom did not want to look at the book," I said. "Why?"

Dad looked nervous. "You will have to ask your mother," he said.

"Did I do something wrong?" I asked Mom. She wrapped her arms around me.

"No," she said. "I cannot read."

Story Comprehension

Think about "The Wednesday Surprise." Finish each sentence by underlining the answer.

1. Grandma takes care of Anna _____ .

   a. every day

   b. only on Wednesdays

2. Anna's dad is a _____ .

   a. truck driver

   b. pilot

3. Anna and Grandma want to surprise Dad because _____ .

   a. it is his birthday

   b. he got a new job

4. Anna and Grandma have worked together to _____ .

   a. teach Anna how to read

   b. teach Grandma how to read

5. Sam and Anna decorate the house because _____ .

   a. it is Dad's birthday

   b. it is a holiday

6. Grandma doesn't have seconds because _____ .

   a. she is thinking about reading

   b. she is full

7. Anna is nervous at the party because _____ .

   a. she wants Grandma to read well

   b. she wants to read well

8. Dad is crying at the end of the story because _____ .

   a. he is sad that his surprise is over

   b. Grandma can read

At Home: Have children draw a picture of their favorite part of the story. Then ask them to write a sentence about it.

Use a Calendar

A **calendar** tells you the month and the day.

NOVEMBER						

Follow the instructions below.

1. The days of the week go in the boxes along the top. Start with Sunday in the first box. What day did you put in the last box?

   _____

2. Start the calendar with November 1 on a Friday. Then put a number in every box. There are thirty days in November. What day of the week is the 25th day? _____

3. Put Thanksgiving in the box for the fourth Thursday of the month. What day of the month is that? _____

4. You have soccer practice every Tuesday. Mark that on the calendar. What dates did you mark? _____

At Home: Have children mark November 17-23 with an **X** and write **vacation** through those days.

Book 2.2/Unit 2
The Wednesday Surprise 4

/ər/ *er*; /ən/ *en*; /əl/ *le*

Write the missing letters in each word. Read the word.

er	en	le

1.

wat _____

2.

cand _____

3.

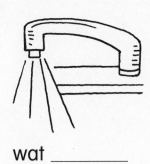

op _____

4.

teach _____

5.

app _____

6.

elev _____

Book 2.2/Unit 2
The Wednesday Surprise

At Home: Help children draw and label a picture
with a word that has one of the endings taught
on this page.

/ər/, /ən/, /əl/; /ü/; /ôr/; /îr/

Read the sentence. Circle the word that completes the sentence. Then write the word on the line.

1. I wore my _____ today.

rooms   boots   shoot

2. Have I met you _____?

tore   more   before

3. I pour _____ into the glass.

either   water   shatter

4. The horse is in the _____.

apple   candle   stable

5. I use my _____ to pick up the peas.

fork   horn   born

6. Everything he said is _____.

blue   true   glue

7. He is seven _____ old.

tears   near   years

8. We had _____ for dinner.

chicken   taken   even

At Home: Have children develop one of the sentences into a one-paragraph story.

Summarize

A summary is a review of the most important points of a story.

Read each story. Give each story a title. Then write a one-sentence **summary** of each story.

Title: _____

    Mr. Green and Mrs. Lopez wanted to plant a garden for our town. They invited people to a meeting. Many people came to talk about the garden. Mr. Wong said he had an empty lot. Anna Lee said she had tools. Everyone agreed to come on Saturday to begin work on a garden.

Summary: _____

Title: _____

    On Saturday, five families came to the lot. We all worked hard. First we took away the trash. Then we dug out the rocks. On Sunday, more people came. They helped to plant seeds. Everyone worked together to make a town garden!

Summary: _____

At Home: After reading the story "The Wednesday Surprise," ask children to retell it in one or two sentences.

Suffixes

The suffixes **-ly** and **-ful** change the meaning of the base word to which they are added. The suffix **-ly** means "in the way of." The suffix **-ful** means "full of."

Write a word that means the same as the group of words. Your new word will end in **-ly** or **-ful.**

1. full of power

    _____

2. in a beautiful way

    _____

3. in a cold way

    _____

4. in a different way

    _____

5. full of thanks

    _____

6. in a soft way

    _____

7. in a bright way

    _____

8. full of good cheer

    _____

Write two sentences using some of the new words.

9. _____

    _____

10. _____

    _____

At Home: Ask children to make a list of other words ending in **-ful** and **-ly**.

Book 2.2/Unit 2
The Wednesday Surprise
10

/ou/ *ow, ou* and /oi/ *oi, oy*

Read each word. Then circle the word next to it that has the same vowel sound.

1. found	howl toy		**2. how**	soil mouth
3. ground	clown soil		**4. point**	loyal pound
5. mouth	boys pout		**6. sound**	noise shout
7. soil	toys cloud		**8. town**	soil cloud
9. boy	ground soil		**10. noise**	broil clown
11. cow	now new		**12. royal**	loan noise

12 Book 2.2/Unit 3
Fossils Tell of Long Ago

At Home: Ask children to think of words that rhyme with words from this page.

193

Vocabulary

Choose a word from the box to finish each sentence.
Write the answers in the puzzle.

buried   creatures   fossil   fresh   layers   millions

Across

3. Some fossils are _____ of
years old.

_____

5. Many _____ live in that lake.

_____

6. The cake had three _____.

_____

Down

1. Luis has a _____ of a fish.

_____

2. My dog _____ a bone in the
yard.

_____

4. I like to eat _____ fruit.

_____

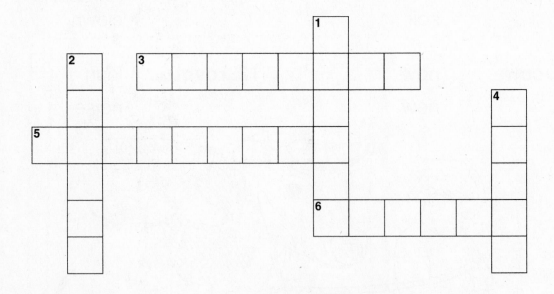

At Home: Have children make a new puzzle with the
words in the box.

Book 2.2/Unit 2
Fossils Tell of Long Ago

6

The
Dinosaur

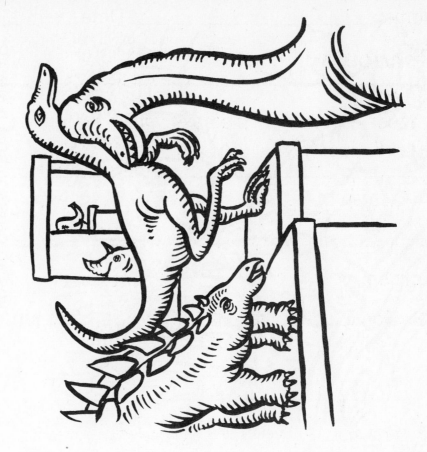

... touched the fossil.

"Wow!" he shouted. He said it was important.

Now people look at the fossil every day. It is the star of the museum. And it is still as tall as the clouds!

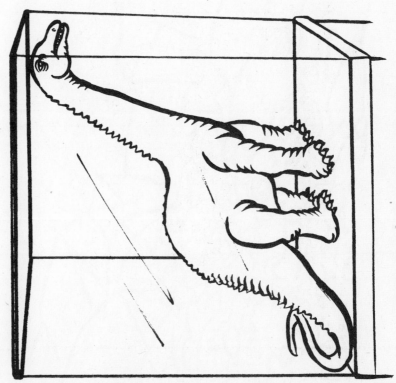

At Home: Have children think about the different kinds of things that might become fossils.

4

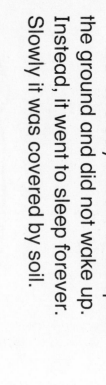

It was one of the creatures from long ago. It ate grass and drank fresh water. It was as tall as the clouds!

But one day it went to sleep on the ground and did not wake up. Instead, it went to sleep forever. Slowly it was covered by soil.

Fossils Tell of Long Ago McGraw-Hill School Division

Millions of years went by. It turned to stone. That is what happens when something is buried under many layers of soil. It was a fossil.

Then one day a crowd of people came. They dug down through all that soil and those layers of mud.

Story Comprehension

Think about what you learned from the story "Fossils Tell of Long Ago." Then answer these questions.

I. Does every animal turn into a fossil?

_____

2. What kinds of things can become fossils?

_____

3. Name three things we can learn from fossils. _____

_____

_____

_____

_____

_____

_____

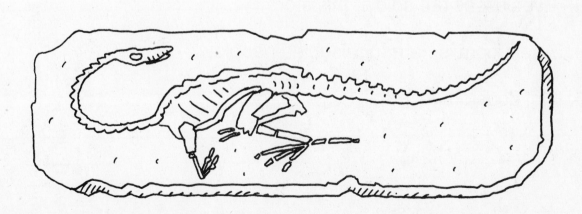

5 Book 2.2/Unit 2
Fossils Tell of Long Ago

At Home: Have children make a drawing of a fossil
that they would like to find.

195

Interpret Signs

Find the signs that show the messages listed below. Write the letter of the sign on the line beside each message.

A.

B.

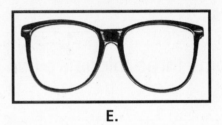
C.

D.

E.

Messages:

1. The road is splitting up ahead to the

   right and to the left. _____

2. Here is the dinosaur museum. _____

3. Eyeglasses are sold in this store. _____

4. A restroom is here for disabled people. _____

5. Hot dogs are for sale. _____

At Home: Have children draw pictures of any signs that they see on the way home from school. Explain the meanings of these signs.

196

Book 2.2/Unit 2
Fossils Tell of Long Ago

5

/ou/ *ow*, *ou* and /oi/ *oi, oy*

Write the words from the list that have the same sound as **ou** in **mouth** or **oi** in **soil**. Then circle the letters in each word that create the sound.

ground	how	south	point
foil	loud	joy	spoil
boy	sound	now	toy
soil	cow	join	found

mouth

1. _____

2. _____

3. _____

4. _____

5. _____

6. _____

7. _____

8. _____

soil

9. _____

10. _____

11. _____

12. _____

13. _____

14. _____

15. _____

16. _____

At Home: Recite the words, "How now, brown cow?"
Encourage children to write a one-line verse using
words from the page.

/ou/; /oi/; /ər/, /ən/, /əl/; /âr/

Choose the word from the box that completes the
sentence. Write the word on the line.

careful	sour	frozen	foil	pickle	ground

1. The lake is _____ in the winter.

2. My hat fell to the _____.

3. Would you like a _____ with your sandwich?

4. Be _____ not to slip and fall.

5. Wrap your sandwich in _____.

6. The lemon tastes _____.

Now draw a line from the sentence to the word that
completes it.

7. The naughty pup was in _____.   point

8. I _____ my shoe under the bed.   smaller

9. This pencil has a sharp _____.   found

10. The duck is _____ than the elephant.   trouble

At Home: Have children write questions using some of
the words above.

Book 2.2/Unit 2
Fossils Tell of Long Ago   10

Sequence of Events

Read the story and the sentences below it. Write **1**, **2**, **3**, **4**, **5**, or **6** next to each sentence to show the order of the story events.

Drew watched as the big moving van pulled up to his house. He wondered how the movers would get everything packed into the van. First they wrapped all the dishes and packed them into boxes. Then they packed clothes and other things into more boxes.

The next day the movers carried all the furniture to the van. Then they placed all the boxes around the furniture. Drew waved good-bye to the movers as they backed the van out of his driveway.

_____ The boxes are placed around the furniture.

_____ The furniture is placed in the van.

_____ Drew sees the moving van come to his house.

_____ Drew waves good-bye to the movers.

_____ The movers pack the dishes.

_____ The movers pack clothes.

6 Book 2.2/Unit 2
Fossils Tell of Long Ago

At Home: Have children tell each other the steps involved in tying their shoes or putting on a jacket.

199

Context Clues

Sometimes you can figure out the meaning of unfamiliar words by looking at the words around them.

Read the story. Some of the underlined words will be new to you. Look for clues to discover each new word's meaning.

In the Desert

Rob and Jill went for a walk in the <u>desert</u>. The air was hot and dry. The ground was hot and dry too. The <u>soil</u> was mostly sand so few plants grew there. Jill saw <u>tracks</u> made by the feet of small animals. She knew <u>creatures</u> like mice and lizards had walked there. When Rob looked for <u>minerals</u>, he found some interesting red rocks and brown rocks. He rubbed and <u>polished</u> a stone to make it shiny.

Draw a line from the word in the first column to its definition in the second.

1. desert		animals
2. soil		marks made by feet
3. tracks		rubbed to make shiny
4. creatures		a dry and hot place
5. minerals		what rocks are made of
6. polished		the top layer of earth, where plants grow

At Home: Ask children to tell you what context clues they used to figure out the meanings of the words in the exercise.

200

Book 2.2/Unit 2
Fossils Tell of Long Ago

6

/ou/; /oi/; /ər/, /ən/, /əl/; /ü/

Read the words on the list. List each one underneath the word that shares the same underlined sound. Then cross the word off the list.

found	apple	river	cow	noise	seven
giggle	blue	toy	open	too	teacher

m<u>ou</u>th

1. _____

2. _____

ov<u>er</u>

7. _____

8. _____

b<u>oo</u>t

3. _____

4. _____

cand<u>le</u>

9. _____

10. _____

happ<u>en</u>

5. _____

6. _____

s<u>oi</u>l

11. _____

12. _____

At Home: Have children circle the letters in each
word that create the underlined sound.

Vocabulary

Read each group of sentences. One word is missing from each group. Find the missing word and fill in the circle next to it.

1. Billy is making a birthday card. He is using _____ to stick a picture on the inside.

○ **a.** soap   ○ **b.** glue   ○ **c.** hurry

2. The picture shows a lion near a tree. Billy cut it out of a _____ .

○ **a.** magazine   ○ **b.** homework   ○ **c.** garden

3. Sally and Becky played out in the rain. They got wet. Now they have to _____ their clothes.

○ **a.** grow   ○ **b.** sell   ○ **c.** change

4. Sally and Becky are playing with blocks. They can't find the red one. They will have to _____ for it.

○ **a.** hunt   ○ **b.** worry   ○ **c.** sing

5. Emile has trouble chewing. Last night he lost a _____. He thought it would come out last week. It took a long time.

○ **a.** card   ○ **b.** tooth   ○ **c.** dog

6. Emile's mother made an apple pie. She cut it and gave him a _____ of it. The pie was soft and tasted good!

○ **a.** piece   ○ **b.** door   ○ **c.** week

Amber's Hunt

in the front of her mouth a huge tooth had grown in.

"Aha!" said Amber. "Here is the missing piece to my life! I don't have to change my life. Now I have everything I need!"

And from that day on Amber felt happy!

At Home: Help children remember a time they wanted something to change. What did they do to make that change happen?

4

Amber the dinosaur wanted to change her life. "I want something new to happen," she said. She picked up a magazine. "I will hunt through the pages to see what I can find."

But the magazine did not have what she was looking for.

Are You a Fossil Fan? McGraw-Hill School Division

Amber tossed a coin. "Heads, I get a new job. Tails, I travel."

But the coin fell into a jar of glue on Amber's table. Amber could not get it out.

"Now I will never know what to do!" she cried.

Just then Amber felt a pain in her mouth.

"Ouch!"

Story Comprehension

Think about what you read in "Are You a Fossil Fan?" Read the sentences and answer the questions.

1. How did Sam Girouard become a fossil finder?

_____

_____

2. How does Sam find fossils?

_____

_____

3. What were two fossils that Sam found?

_____

_____

4. What is unusual about Sam?

_____

5. Would you like to meet Sam? Why or why not?

_____

_____

5 | Book 2.2/Unit 2
Are You a Fossil Fan?

At Home: Ask the children to share facts with you that they remember about fossils.

203

Read an Ad

Look at the **advertisements** shown below. Decide if each ad is trying to get you to buy something or to do something.

Write **Buy Something** on the blank line if the ad is selling a product. Write **Do Something** if the ad is trying to change your opinion or get you to do something.

Advertising Language:

1. **AT $29.95 THIS IS A GIVEAWAY OFFER!** You won't find rain boots like this anywhere else in the city. Act now and we'll throw in a **FREE UMBRELLA!** _____

2. *How would you like it if we dumped our garbage can in the middle of your living room!* DON'T LITTER! IT'S DIRTY AND UGLY, AND IT'S NOT POLITE! _____

3. Is your house always cold? Add **Solar Windows** and get warm today. _____

4. You wouldn't wear clothes someone else picked out for you. You wouldn't drive someone else's car. So why let somebody else pick your government? **GET OUT AND VOTE.** _____

5. Happiness is a state of mind. Peace is found in living right. Take it easy. Drink Orange Juice. It's just good. _____

At Home: Help children to make a collage with advertisements clipped from magazines. Ask them whether each ad is trying to get them to buy or to do something.

Sequence of Events

Read the story. Number the pictures to show the order in which they happened in the story.

Grandpa Jake makes the best vegetable soup. First, he boils water in a big pot. Then, he peels carrots and puts them in the pot. Next, he adds corn and green beans. After that, he cuts up potatoes and places them in with everything else to cook. Finally, he adds his own special spices to the soup. My favorite part is eating the soup with fresh bread!

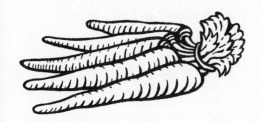
_____

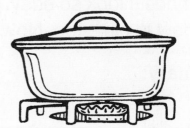
_____

_____

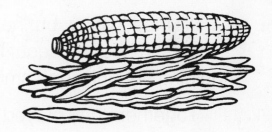
_____

_____

_____

6 Book 2.2/Unit 2
Are You a Fossil Fan?

At Home: Ask children to explain the steps they take to make a favorite food. Ask what would happen if they forgot a step or made it in the wrong order.

205

Summarize

A **summary** is a short way to tell what happens in a story. A summary tells the most important information in a sentence or two.

Read each story, and write a summary. Remember to write each summary in one or two sentences.

Jill opened the black case and looked inside. It was a shiny, new violin. Jill plucked a string. I will never, ever learn to play! she thought.

Jill's brother Owen played the violin very well. He made it look so easy. Jill had always wanted to learn how to play, too. Now she wondered if she could do it.

Summary:_____

_____

_____

Jill tried to play, but her violin sounded like a sad cat. Then she heard a beautiful sound behind her. Owen was holding his violin and smiling. "I'll play with you," he said.

Together, they played the song over and over. When Owen stopped playing, Jill had a surprise. Music was coming from her own violin! Owen grinned. "All it takes is practice," he said.

Summary: _____

_____

_____

At Home: Help children to practice summarizing stories by inviting them to summarize the plot of a cartoon.

Book 2.2/ Unit 2
Are You a Fossil Fan? 2

Context Clues

Read the story. Find clues to the meaning of the underlined words by reading the words around them. Then choose one of the underlined words to answer each question.

Animals in the Snow

Many animals can live in snow. In the coldest winters, the earth is <u>frozen</u> hard. Rabbits and foxes dig holes in the snow to live in. They lie happily <u>buried</u> under a snow bank. They are warm and safe, <u>protected</u> from the cold winds. Some bigger animals, such as the <u>mammoth</u> who lived long ago and the polar bear, can live where it is cold all year. They have warm <u>layers</u> of fat and fur.

1. To be safe and warm is to be _____.

2. To lie underneath something is to be _____.

3. When something grows cold and hard, it is _____.

4. One big animal that lived long ago was the _____.

5. Thicknesses or coats of something are called _____.

5 Book 2.2/Unit 2
Are You a Fossil Fan?

At Home: Have children draw an illustration for the story and use two of the underlined words to write a caption.

207

Suffixes

Choose a word from the box that means the same as the phrase in parentheses. Rewrite the sentence using the new word.

quickly	slowly	skillful	fearful	helpful	neatly

1. We ate our lunch (in a slow way).

_____

2. Matt is (full of skill) with a hammer.

_____

3. The rain fell (in a quick way.)

_____

4. Do not be (full of fear) when it is dark.

_____

5. Mom was (full of help) with my science project.

_____

6. Lola wrote (in a neat way).

_____

208

At Home: Help children make a list of all the words they have learned that end in **-ly** and **-ful**.

Book 2.2/Unit 2
Are You a Fossil Fan?
6

Unit 2 Vocabulary Review

A. Put a check mark next to each true sentence.

_____ 1. People can play <u>music</u> on a piano.

_____ 2. Your <u>favorite</u> food is the food that you like best.

_____ 3. People play baseball in an <u>office</u>.

_____ 4. People <u>glue</u> things to hold them together.

_____ 5. You can taste a <u>voice</u>.

B. Complete the crossword puzzle using the words in the box.

magazine	scare	field	daughter	wrapped

DOWN

1. He read a ___ while he
    waited.

2. I ___ his gift in paper.

ACROSS

3. They have one ___ and three
    sons.

4. The noise will ___ the birds
    away.

5. The baseball team ran onto
    the ___ .

10 Book 2.2/Unit 2
Unit 2 Vocabulary Review

At Home: Have children write a paragraph using
three of the words above.

209

Unit 2 Vocabulary Review

A. Circle the word that means the opposite of each word.

I. heavy

    a. big   **b.** light   **c.** little

2. nervous

    a. calm   **b.** scared   **c.** smart

3. millions

    a. many   **b.** two   **c.** none

4. score

    a. win a point   **b.** lose a point   **c.** cook

B. Write the word to complete the questions.
Then, answer **Yes** or **No** to the questions.

chance	whistle	touch	piece

I. Do you know how to _____? _____

2. Would you _____ a wild lion? _____

3. If you had a _____ to ride on a roller coaster,

    would you? _____

4. Have you ever eaten a _____ of pizza? _____

At Home: Have children write one true sentence and
one false sentence for some of the words above.

Book 2.2/Unit 2
Unit 2 Vocabulary Review

8

Digraphs *ph, tch, ch*

Read the following words.

phone	wa**tch**	spee**ch**

Circle the word that answers each clue. Then write the word.

1. This is something you talk into.

chair   telephone   watch

_____

2. This means to shout for joy.

cheer   children   match

_____

3. This is something you can sit on.

chair   speeches   catch

_____

4. This is a talk given to a group.

telephone checked speech

_____

5. This is what you do at the movies.

latch   chicken   watch

_____

6. This is what you get with a camera.

phone   photo   bench

_____

7. This is when you grab something.

catch   cheered   watch

_____

8. This is a very large animal.

chicken   patch   elephant

_____

16 Book 2.2/Unit 3
Officer Buckle and Gloria

At Home: Have children find pictures of words that have **ch, tch,** or **ph** in them.

211

Vocabulary

Choose a word from the box to complete each sentence.
Write the words on the lines. Each word is used twice.

| accidents | audience | cheered | slips | station | wipe |

1. The train came into the _____ early.

   Everyone shouted and _____.

2. The children _____ when the clown came out.

   He said they were a good _____.

3. Jake _____ and falls every day.

   He has too many _____!

4. Please _____ up the water that spilled.

   Someone from the _____ might fall.

5. Many people had car _____ yesterday.

   Some of the people went to the police _____.

6. Arthur forgets to _____ the mud off his shoes.

   He _____ on the floor.

At Home: Ask children to draw a picture to illustrate each sentence.

Book 2.2/Unit 3
Officer Buckle and Gloria
12

Chad and the Horses

Then they all saw why the horse fell.

There was water on the floor.

Mark said, "I spilled water. I forgot to wipe it up. I'm sorry."

Luckily the horse was fine.

Everyone forgave Mark. From that day on he tried not to rush the horses.

At Home: Review with the children how the animals in this story danced for work. What are some other animals that work? What do they do?

4

Chad's father had beautiful horses. Every summer, the horses would perform in shows. The audience loved the shows.

Chad liked it when the children cheered for the horses. He also loved the speeches his father would make.

Chad and his brother Mark helped their father by bringing the horses water.

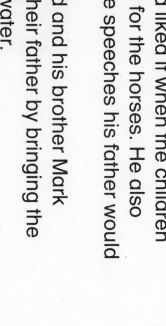

"We don't want any accidents," Chad's father said. "Wipe up all spilled water, so no horse or person slips."

Chad was very careful. Everyone liked Chad, even the horses. They did not like Mark. Mark always hurried the horses.

One day Chad was watching the show from the water station near the door. Suddenly a horse slipped and fell.

Story Comprehension

Answer each question about "Officer Buckle and Gloria."

1. In Napville, who knew more safety tips than anyone else?

   _____

2. What was one of Officer Buckle's safety tips?

   _____

   _____

3. What did Gloria do while Officer Buckle gave speeches?

   _____

4. What did Officer Buckle think Gloria was doing while he was making speeches?

   _____

5. How did Officer Buckle find out what Gloria was doing?

   _____

   _____

6. What was Officer Buckle's best safety tip?

   _____

6 Book 2.2/Unit 3
Officer Buckle and Gloria

At Home: Have children tell which trick of Gloria's was their favorite.

213

Do a Subject Search at the Library

When writing a report or looking for information, a computer **subject search** will give you a number of books to choose from.

Search of South Millford Library System

Search:	Pumpkins

Items Found = 28

[X] First Ten   [ ] Second Ten   [ ] Third Ten

1. Title: *The Greatest Pumpkin Ever* Fiction
   Author: Hemsley Yorborough
   ■ **See Full Record**
   Pub. Date: ©1994

2. Title: *Pumpkin Pie Baking*
   Author: Nancy Edlands
   ■ **See Full Record**
   Pub Date: ©1999

3. Title: *Grow the Big Ones*
   Author: Ray Moncliff
   ■ **See Full Record**
   Pub. Date: ©1979

4. Title: *Pumping Iron for More Muscle*
   Author: Quincy Cummings
   ■ **See Full Record**
   Pub. Date: ©1989 Video recording

Use the results of the subject search shown above to answer the questions.

1. Which book would help you with baking a pumpkin pie?

_____

2. Which book would help you with producing large pumpkins in your garden? _____

3. Which book is fiction, or a made-up story? _____

_____

4. Which book looks like it has nothing to do with pumpkins?

(Hint: sometimes the computer confuses words that look alike.

Pumpkin could be seen by the computer as Pump or kin.)

_____

At Home: Ask the children which of the books listed above was published most recently.

Digraphs *ph, tch, ch*

Complete the sentences.

cheered	chair	phone	watched	children
speech	photograph	match	elephant	hatch

1. The _____ love to play games.

2. Brian gave a _____ to the class about jokes.

3. The team _____ when they won the game.

4. Betsy used the _____ to call her mother.

5. Ricky _____ the bird fly from the tree.

6. Tom sat in the _____.

7. The huge _____ walked to the pond.

8. It was exciting to see the chick _____.

9. Sally tried to find the _____ for her shoe.

10. I took a _____ of my brother.

At Home: Ask children to make a chart of words with **ch, tch,** and **ph.** Then encourage them to write a sentence that uses two of these words.

Digraphs *ph, tch, ch*

Use the words in the box to answer the riddles.
Write the answers on the lines.

telephone	child	stitch	photos	watch
chair	rich	chase	scratch	patch

1. I tell you the time. What am I? _____

2. I ring and you pick me up. What am I? _____

3. You can sit in me. What am I? _____

4. You make me with a needle and thread. What am I? _____

5. I have not grown up yet. What am I? _____

Choose a word from the box above to complete the
following sentences.

6. Lindsey took _____ on her trip.

7. You can _____ your jeans if they rip.

8. The dog likes to _____ the cat up a tree.

9. I have a lot of money. I am _____.

10. Don't _____ yourself on the sharp thorns.

At Home: Have children write a riddle for the word
cheese.

Form Generalizations

Read the story about Spike and Ike. Then answer the questions that follow.

>   Spike is Ryan's dog. Ike is his cat. Spike chased Ike up a tree. Spike chased a squirrel up the tree, too. Ryan had to get Ike down. Ryan put Spike on a leash after he chased the mail carrier. But that didn't stop Spike. He barked at the birds and tried to chase them into the next yard.

What are the facts?

Spike chased _____

Spike chased _____

Spike chased _____

Spike chased _____

Write a generalization about Spike.

_____

_____

At Home: Have children think about the actions of other pets, such as cats, birds, or hamsters. Have them make a generalization about one animal's behavior.

Multiple-Meaning Words

The underlined words in the following sentences have more than one meaning. Read each sentence. Look for clues that tell you which meaning is being used. Fill in the circle next to the meaning of the underlined word.

1. The little dog can catch the stick.

    ⓐ a piece of wood

    ⓑ to be held fast

2. His paws will stick in the mud.

    ⓐ a piece of wood

    ⓑ to be held fast

3. The dog wore a checked shirt.

    ⓐ tested to see if things were as they should be

    ⓑ marked with different-colored squares

4. He checked for food in his dish.

    ⓐ looked to see

    ⓑ marked with different-colored squares

5. Please do not tip over the milk!

    ⓐ to turn over

    ⓑ a round or pointed end

6. There is a fly on the tip of his nose.

    ⓐ to turn over

    ⓑ a round or pointed end

At Home: Invite children to think of another word that has two meanings. Have them use each meaning in a sentence.

218

Book 2.2/Unit 3
Officer Buckle and Gloria
6

Long *e, i*

Complete each sentence with a word from the box.

green	sweet	piece	trees
teaches	leader	climb	brightly
line	bike	fine	kite

1. The sun is shining very _____.

2. The grass is _____.

3. Ice cream is _____.

4. Joe likes follow-the-_____.

5. Lucy loves to climb _____.

6. Karen _____ music.

7. Tim and Nora _____ to the top.

8. Luis has a _____ of apple.

9. Nancy drew a _____ on the paper.

10. Harold rode his _____ to school.

11. He had to pay a _____ for the late book.

12. They all wanted to fly the _____.

Vocabulary

Read the story. Choose a word from the box to complete each sentence. Write the word in the sentence. Then reread the story to check your answers.

borrow	desert	evenings	midnight	package	shoulder

Larry wanted to _____ a book from

Tony. He walked up behind Tony and tapped him on the

_____. "May I borrow your book?" he asked.

Tony handed Larry a _____. The book was

inside.

The book was about life in the _____. It

had pictures of plants and animals. A desert is very hot.

Some animals sleep in the daytime. They come out in the

_____ when it is cool. Some even hunt as late

as _____. Larry liked the book. He hopes to

visit a desert someday.

220
At Home: Have children write another story using the vocabulary words.
Book 2.2/Unit 3
Tomás and the Library Lady
6

A Pet for My Pet

I asked my dad what he thought.
He told me he had an idea. Then he
left the hotel.

Later that night he returned with a
brown package. It was about the size
of my lizard. Quickly I opened the
box. It was another lizard.

"I think your pet needs a pet,"
said Dad. I think he was right!

4

220a

2

We live in the desert. It is very hot during the day. In the evenings it can be very cool.

I have a pet lizard. He likes to sit on my shoulder as I do my homework. He also likes to climb into my closet.

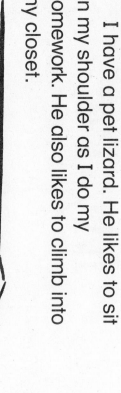

Last week I had to borrow a cage for my lizard. We were going on vacation and I did not want to leave her.

The drive to the beach was very long. We did not get to our hotel until midnight. My lizard was fast asleep as we unpacked the car.

Our vacation by the beach was fun. But my lizard seemed sad. I did not know what was wrong.

Story Comprehension

Think about "Tomás and the Library Lady." Finish each sentence by writing in the correct answer from the choices below.

I. Tomás moves from Texas to

_____

a. Iowa
b. Mexico

2. Tomás's parents work

_____

a. in the farm fields
b. in a school

3. Papá Grande is the best

_____

a. cook in the family
b. storyteller in the family

4. Tomás goes to the library

to find _____

a. story books
b. a teacher

5. The library lady finds many

_____

a. books for Tomás
b. shells for Tomás

6. Tomás teaches

_____

a. Spanish words to the library lady
b. other children how to read

7. When Tomás must return to Texas,

_____

a. he is afraid to go to the library
b. he brings sweet cake to the library lady

8. The library lady gives Tomás

_____

a. a shiny new book
b. a box of candy

8

Book 2.2/Unit 3
Tomás and the Library Lady

At Home: Take children to a local library and have them choose a book to read.

221

Read a Library Floor Plan

A **library floor plan** is a small map of the library. The **circulation desk**, where you can check out and return books, is usually near the door.

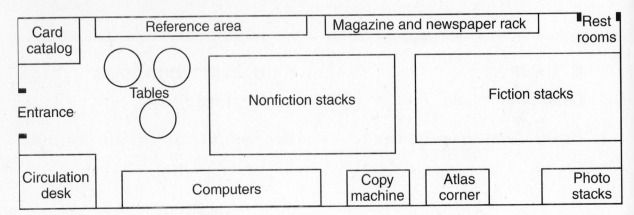

Answer the questions.

1. What are found straight ahead of you as you enter the

   library? _____

2. Which stacks are closest to the restrooms?

   _____

3. What library part would you go to for a book of maps?

   _____

4. Is the reference area closer to the photo stacks or the

   computers? _____

5. What is next to the left of the magazine and newspaper area?

   _____

At Home: Encourage children to list subjects that interest them. Then bring children to the library and search for books on these subjects

222

Book 2.2/Unit 3
Tomás and the Library Lady

5

Long *e, i*

Circle the word that completes the sentence. Then write
the word on the line.

1. Brush your _____ every day.

    tree   teeth   iron

2. Letty is going to _____ a mountain.

    climb   cry   teach

3. The animals came back one _____ one.

    tree   green   by

4. After two hours, the bus _____ came.

    finally   peeked   leaves

5. Millie loves to jump into a huge pile of _____.

    midnight   iron   leaves

6. Kay's mother mowed the _____ grass.

    green   eager   teach

12 Book 2.2/Unit 3
Tomás and the Library Lady

At Home: Ask children to make up another sentence
using one of the words they circled.

223

Long e; Long i; tch, ch

Write a word from the box to complete each rhyme.

chair	kind	tree	fly	steal
light	piece	hatch	pie	tea

1. "Sit in a _____," I said to the bear.

2. Some birds _____ up in the sky.

3. I climbed a _____ near the sea.

4. Turn off the _____. It is too bright.

5. Give this _____ to the geese.

6. That thief wants to _____ my orange peel!

7. I like to catch chicks when they _____.

8. She said, "I find you to be _____."

9. You didn't lie; you ate my _____.

10. The honey in my _____ was made by a bee.

224
At Home: Have children make up a rhyme using the word **green** and illustrate it.

Book 2.2/Unit 3
Tomás and the Library Lady
10

Main Idea

Read each story. Underline the answers to the questions.

Ladybugs are insects that are important to farmers and gardeners. Ladybugs eat the tiny insects that eat the leaves of plants. This allows the plants to grow big and strong. Some farmers welcome the orange and black ladybugs. Using ladybugs is better than using bug spray.

1. What is the main idea?
   a. Ladybugs live in gardens.
   b. Ladybugs are important insects.
   c. Ladybugs like farmers.

2. What do ladybugs eat?
   a. They eat healthy plants.
   b. They eat orange and black spray.
   c. They eat tiny insects.

Jill always likes helping her dad work in his wood shop. She sweeps up small pieces of wood that fall on the floor. She also stacks the new boards in straight piles. Sometimes her dad lets her use a hammer to pound nails into the wooden toys he makes. That is her favorite thing to do.

3. What is the main idea?
   a. Jill makes toys.
   b. Jill likes wood.
   c. Jill likes to help in the wood shop.

4. What does Jill like to do most?
   a. She likes to pound nails with a hammer.
   b. She likes to sweep the floor.
   c. She likes to stack boards.

4 Book 2.2/Unit 3
Tomás and the Library Lady

At Home: Ask children to name one detail that supports each main idea.

225

Multiple-Meaning Words

Read each sentence. Write the meaning of the underlined word on the line after each sentence.

1. Dad always <u>leaves</u> early. _____

2. The bus turned <u>right</u> at the corner. _____

3. Burt can throw the <u>ball</u> across the field. _____

4. The <u>light</u> by her bed was off. _____

5. We put the <u>leaves</u> in a big pile. _____

6. I got the <u>right</u> answer. _____

7. A balloon floats because it is <u>light</u>. _____

8. The leaves turn brown every <u>fall</u>. _____

9. Cinderella met a prince at the <u>ball</u>. _____

10. The children will <u>watch</u> the show. _____

11. I always <u>fall</u> on the ice in the winter. _____

12. He was late, and he kept looking at his <u>watch</u>. _____

_____

At Home: Ask children to think of another word that has two meanings. Have them draw a picture to illustrate each meaning.

226

Book 2.2/Unit 3
Tomás and the Library Lady
12

Long *a, o*

Complete each sentence with a word from the box below.

show	yellow	plain	raincoat	way	day	maid	toes

1. Could you _____ me the picture?

2. Polly knows the _____ across the lake .

3. Henry colors the sun _____.

4. The _____ cleaned the room.

5. I wear my _____ when it rains.

6. May said that her fingers and _____

   were cold.

7. Sue wore a _____ dress to the party.

8. Today is a sunny _____.

⟨8⟩ Book 2.2/Unit 3
Princess Pooh

At Home: Ask children to think of more words that
contain the sounds of long **a** spelled **ai, ay** and long
o, spelled **oa, oe,** and **ow.**

227

Vocabulary

Read the words in the box. Read the clues. Write the correct word on the line below each clue.

cousins	crowded	golden	princess	restaurant	world

1. This person might sit on a throne.

   _____

2. We like to go here when we're hungry.

   _____

3. These are people in your family you might visit.

   _____

4. During a big sale, a store might be like this.

   _____

5. A king might wear a crown this color.

   _____

6. You might fly around this in a plane someday.

   _____

228

At Home: Have children make up new riddles for the vocabulary words.

Book 2.2/Unit 3
Princess Pooh
6

The Princess
With a Heart

not Rita? She has long, beautiful hair."

He said, "I want someone who can see outside her window."

"What could he mean?" asked Rita. One day she left the mirror and looked out her window. Since that day Rita stopped looking in the mirror.

One day she saw a prince below her window. Soon they were married!

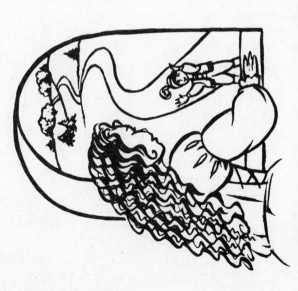

At Home: Have children write the next page for this book. Suggest they begin by telling what happened next to Princess Rita.

4

Once there was a princess named
Rita. She and her sisters, Maria and
Nina, lived in a golden palace.

Rita's sisters, Maria and Nina,
worked hard every day. Rita braided
her long, black hair.

Sometimes Maria and Nina
would ask their sister to help. Rita
always said no. She was too busy
looking in the mirror.

Princess Pooh McGraw-Hill School Division

...e day a prince showed up
from another part of the world. He
asked Nina to marry him.

All of the girls' cousins and
friends came to the wedding at a
fancy restaurant. It was very
crowded. Another prince also came.
He asked Maria to marry him.

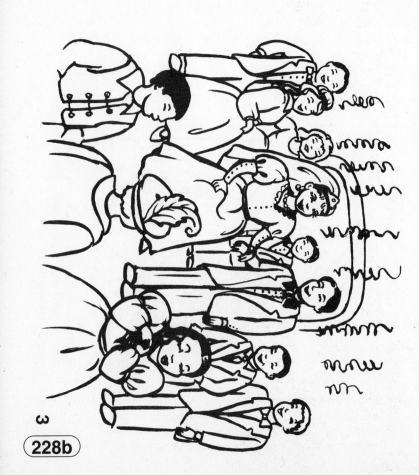

3

Story Comprehension

Think about "Princess Pooh." Draw a line to match the beginning of each sentence with the end.

1. Princess Pooh   says Penelope is wonderful.

2. Patty Jean Piper   cleans the bathroom on Saturdays.

3. Grandma   must sit in a wheelchair.

4. Dad   carries Princess Pooh's throne in his car.

5. Carnival Man   takes Princess Pooh to therapy.

6. Mom   gives Penelope a prize.

At Home: Ask children to tell how Patty Jean felt about her sister at the beginning of the story and then at the end. What made her change her mind?

Use an Encyclopedia

One of the best ways to learn more about a subject is to look at more than one entry in an encyclopedia. Sometimes an entry will direct you to another entry that contains related information.

BUMBLEBEE is a large, hairy, black and yellow bee that is often seen in summer. Bumblebees live in almost every country. Some islands in the Pacific never had bumblebees until man brought them. They range in size from one half to one inch. Unlike honeybees, they do not die after they sting. Bumblebees can sting again and again. They make a loud buzzing noise as they fly, scaring many people. The enemies of the bumblebee are beetles, flies, ants, mites, and wasps. *See also: Bee, Clover*

BEE is an insect that lives everywhere in the world except near the North and South Poles. There are 10,000 kinds of bees but only the honeybee makes honey. Most people are afraid of bees, but they only sting when scared or hurt. Honeybees are social insects. They live and work in a huge group called a colony. They fly about 12 miles an hour. Bees have been found in amber that was fifty million years old. *See also: Clover, Honey, Pollen, Pupa*

Use the encyclopedia entries to answer the questions.

1. Which entry discusses one kind of bee only? _____

2. What entry does both of these entries tell you to see?

_____

3. What fact about bees do both entries mention?

_____

4. What are the other entries that are suggested for you to read?

_____

At Home: Have children illustrate one of the facts they have learned about bees from the entries above.

230

Book 2.2/Unit 3
Princess Pooh

4

Long *a, o*

Circle the word that best completes each sentence. Then write the word on the line.

1. She _____ what happened.

   knows   row   mow

2. Sarah watches the storm from the _____.

   no   window   yellow

3. The _____ pours down.

   bay   plain   rain

4. A big truck _____ by.

   shows   goes   tows

5. Sarah _____ inside the house until the rain stops.

   main   ways   stays

6. At the end of the storm, she sees a _____.

   rainbow   show   maid

Long *a, o, e, i; tch, ch*

A. Write the word from the box that completes each sentence.

field	high	sky	find	catch

1. I _____ my lost shoe under the bed.

2. If I throw the ball, will you _____ it?

3. We run in the _____ behind my house.

4. The rocket shot up into the _____.

5. How _____ can you jump?

B. Now draw a line from each sentence to the word that completes it.

6. His teeth _____ when he gets cold.   read

7. He will put on his _____ to get warm.   play

8. Do you _____ a lot of books?   chatter

9. I like to _____ baseball.   drain

10. The dirty water went down the _____.   coat

At Home: Have children illustrate one of the sentences above.

Book 2.2/Unit 3
Princess Pooh   10

Form Generalizations

Think about the story "Princess Pooh." Then write the
answer to each question on the line.

1. Why does Patty Jean call Penny Princess Pooh?

_____

_____

_____

2. How does Patty Jean feel about Penny at the beginning of the
   story?

_____

_____

3. How does Patty Jean think that other people feel about Penny?

_____

_____

4. Does Patty Jean think she is treated as well as Penny?

_____

5. Is everyone nice to Patty Jean when she rides in the
   wheelchair? Give examples.

_____

_____

5 Book 2.2/Unit 3
Princess Pooh

At Home: Ask children to make another
generalization about either Patty Jean or Penny.

233

Figurative Language

What picture does each group of words make you think of?

like little stars   like a million dollars

like a great, round orange   as clear as glass

like people marching down the road

Complete each sentence by writing a phrase from above in the space. Use each phrase only once.

I. The trees looked

_____

2. The sun looked

_____

3. The dew on the grass was shining

_____

4. The lake was

_____

5. When I woke up this morning, I felt

_____

Soft *c* and Soft *g*

Complete the words that answer the riddles.

1. This is something that is cold and hard. You can also see through it.

   i_____e

2. This is something that helps you cross over the water.

   brid_____e

3. This is something you must run fast in to win.

   ra_____e

4. These are small furry animals. Most of them like to eat cheese.

   mi_____e

5. This is where small animals are kept.

   ca_____e

6. Lions, tigers, and bears are this word.

   fier_____e

7. This is what you turn in a book.

   pa_____e

8. This is something you can cook on.

   ran_____e

6 Book 2.2/Unit 3
Swimmy

At Home: Have children write a silly sentence using some of the answers on this page.

235

Vocabulary

Read each sentence. Write **T** if the sentence is true.
Write **F** if the sentence if false.

escaped	fierce	hidden	machine	swaying	swift

_____ I. If you are hidden, you can't be seen.

_____ 2. A swift deer moves slowly.

_____ 3. The fish that escaped is free.

_____ 4. If you are swaying, you are very still.

_____ 5. You should be careful around a fierce dog.

_____ 6. If you are a swift runner, you might win the race.

_____ 7. Most machines are very slow.

_____ 8. A fierce animal is friendly to people.

_____ 9. A monkey that has escaped is still in a cage.

_____ 10. If you are hidden, everyone can see you.

_____ I I. A machine can do a lot of work.

_____ 12. The swaying branches on a tree are moving.

At Home: Have children make up other true and false
statements about the vocabulary words.

Going to School

things! Sometimes when I'm afraid I hide in strange places. I dig into the sand. I even hide behind a rock.

My friends and I will stay hidden for hours. Life in the sea is dangerous and exciting!

At Home: Have children draw a picture of a school of fish. Then have them draw some fish hiding behind the rocks.

4

236a

I am a fish who swims in a school. Why do I do this?

Sometimes I swim in a school so I can have fun with my friends.

Sometimes I swim in a school so fierce, big fish will stay away. The big fish see so many of us that they don't know who to eat. The big fish get mad. Finally they give up and we are safe.

Sometimes we are in trouble even when we swim in schools. A huge machine stretches large, swaying nets in the sea. The nets are almost hidden in the dark water. Fish are very swift. But we don't always see what's in front of us. That's when we get stuck in the nets.

Story Comprehension

Think about "Swimmy." Read this passage about "Swimmy."

Swimmy wanted to look all around. But the little red fish were afraid a large fish would eat them. Swimmy wanted to think of some way to have fun.

Write a complete sentence to answer each question.

1. What did Swimmy do right before this part of the story?

_____

_____

2. What did Swimmy do right after this part of the story?

_____

_____

3. What is important about this part of the story?

_____

_____

4. How do you think the little fish would describe Swimmy?

_____

_____

4 Book 2.2/Unit 3
Swimmy

At Home: Ask children to name things that Swimmy and the fish will see as they travel the deep, wet world.

237

Do an Author Search at the Library

When you do an **author search,** it is important to look closely at the description of the books listed. If you click on the icon that says "Full Record," you will find more information about a specific book.

Look at this result list of an author search. Let's say you read *Take Joy: The Tasha Tudor Christmas Book.* Now you want another book about the holidays. What would be a good choice?

1. Title: Take Joy: The Magical World of Tasha Tudor   (video recording)
   Pub. Date: 1996   ■ **See Full Record**
2. Title: A Time to Keep: The Tasha Tudor Book of Holidays
   Pub. Date: 1992   ■ **See Full Record**
3. Title: Take Joy: The Tasha Tudor Christmas Book
   Pub. Date: 1966   ■ **See Full Record**

I. _____

To further help you decide, click on
the Full Record icon. This is what
you'd see. Use this information
to answer the questions that follow.

Title: A Time to Keep: The Tasha Tudor Book of Holidays
Author: Tudor, Tasha
Publisher: Chicago: Rand McNally, © 1977; 58 pages, illustrations
Subjects: holidays in old New England

Library Location	Call Number
Wilson	J 394 TUD
East Treamer	J/394.26974/T

2. What is the subject of this book? _____

3. Which library locations have a copy? _____

_____

4. What is the call number of this book at Wilson library? _____

At Home: Ask children what, besides books, is available by Tasha Tudor. (a videotape)

Soft *c* and Soft *g*

Below are pairs of words. The second word is scrambled.
Unscramble the second word to make it rhyme with the
first word and write your word on the line.

1. range   asgtrne   _____

2. race   epalc   _____

3. rice   inec   _____

4. face   lcea   _____

5. cage   tsgae   _____

6. mice   cei   _____

7. page   gera   _____

8. twice   cmei   _____

9. brace   ctrae   _____

10. wage   gea   _____

11. nice   lisce   _____

12. juice   ecrtu   _____

12   Book 2.2/Unit 3
Swimmy

At Home: Have children write a sentence for two of
the words they formed.

239

Soft *c, g;* Long *a, o, e, i*

Circle, then write, the word that completes each sentence.

1. Can you _____ out all the candles?

   blow   snow   flow

2. I put _____ in my drink.

   ice   mice   dice

3. He made a pot with some _____.

   hay   clay   say

4. The leaves fell from the _____.

   tree   bee   sneeze

5. Pam had a _____ that she could fly.

   leap   cream   dream

6. I use my _____ to think.

   stain   chain   brain

7. I _____ into pajamas before I go to bed.

   change   strange   page

8. Let's take the _____ to the beach.

   hail   train   rain

At Home: Have children write a one-paragraph story based on one of the sentences above.

Book 2.2/Unit 3
Swimmy
8

Main Idea

Details are bits of information that support the main idea.

Read these sentences about "Swimmy." Then write the main idea for each section and one detail that supports it.

A group of little fish lived in a small part of the great ocean. All were red except one of them. The little black fish swam faster than all the rest. Swimmy was his name.

1. **Main Idea:** _____

2. **Detail:** _____

_____

A tuna fish swallowed all the little red fish one day. But Swimmy escaped. He was very sad as he swam away.

3. **Main Idea:** _____

4. **Detail:** _____

Swimmy saw a school of little fish, just like him. They were afraid of the big fish. Swimmy taught them to swim close together like one giant fish.

5. **Main Idea:** _____

6. **Detail:** _____

_____

At Home: Ask children to name one more detail for each main idea on this page.

Figurative Language

A writer will sometimes describe something by comparing it to something else.

Read the first sentence in each pair. Think about the picture the words bring to mind. Then complete the second statement to tell what the first sentence means.

1. My little dog can eat like a horse.

   My little dog can eat _____.

2. The hailstones were the size of baseballs.

   The hailstones were _____.

3. My sister is as light as a feather.

   My sister is not _____.

4. His shirt looked like an old rag.
   His shirt was not _____.

5. Those deer can run like the wind.

   Those deer can run _____.

6. The forest fire spread like lightning.

   The forest fire spread _____.

At Home: Point out that the last two sentences contain sayings that mean "quickly." Ask children to invent two more comparisons that mean the same thing.

Soft *c, g; ph, tch;* Long *a, o, e, i*

Circle the word that names each picture. Then write the word on the line.

1.  ice   iron

   _____

2.  phone   tone

   _____

3.  sea   tree

   _____

4.  catch   watch

   _____

5.  strange   large

   _____

5   Book 2.2/Unit 3
The World's Plants Are in Danger

At Home: Ask children to choose two circled words and write two rhyming words for each one.

243

Vocabulary

Circle the word that best completes the sentence. Then write the word on the line.

1. We have a _____ because our car is broken._____

   door   problem   plant

2. I want to _____ the whales in the ocean. _____

   walk   swim   save

3. Let me _____ you that fire is dangerous. _____

   sing   change   warn

4. I hope my cat will not run away and _____. _____

   disappear   receive   whistle

5. The air is so _____ I can see for miles. _____

   clear   dark   new

6. It seems like _____ since we last went to the beach. _____

   millions   sun   forever

At Home: Have children write a short story using the vocabulary words.

A Dolphin's Giant Save

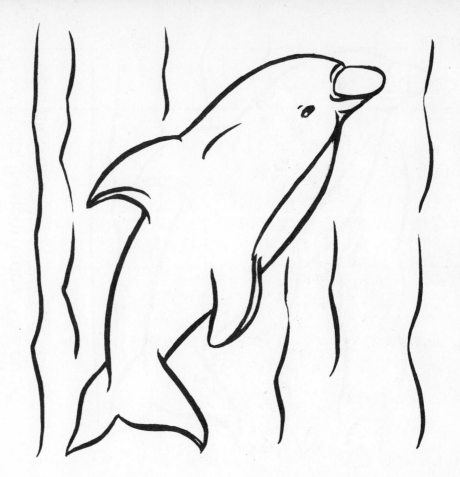

Tracy had to think twice as fast.
She grabbed the seaweed. Quickly
she wrapped it around the giant. He
fell down into the water.

Next Tracy's friends appeared.
"We will help you!" they shouted.
Together the group of dolphins
towed the giant back to shore.

"Let me warn you," Tracy said.
"Don't ever come after me again."

At Home: Have children look in an encyclopedia to
find the answer to this question: Is a dolphin a
mammal or a fish?

4

244a

Long ago, there was a dolphin named Tracy. She lived in a deep sea of clear green water.

One day a giant named Pete came to the shore. "I am going to catch the biggest fish there is," he said.

Uh-oh, thought Tracy. This could be a problem.

The giant came marching into the sea. Poor Tracy tried to disappear behind some seaweed. The giant saw her and grabbed at the plants.

"I know you are in there!" he said. "You can't hide from me forever!"

Tracy didn't know what to do. She had to save herself!

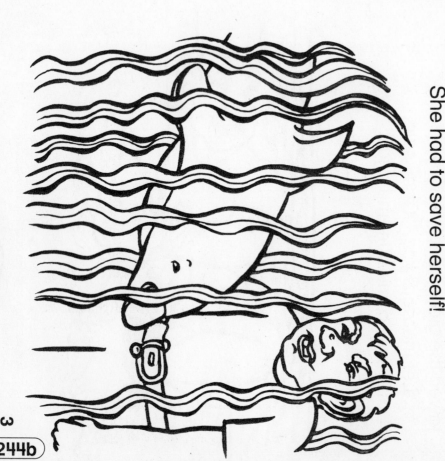

Story Comprehension

Think about "The World's Plants Are in Danger." Circle the correct answer to each question.

1. Why should you not pick wildflowers?

   They may be in danger of disappearing forever.

   They may belong to someone else.

2. About how many types of plants are in trouble?

   about 1,000

   about 34,000

3. What is true about nearly all of the plants in danger?

   Each kind grows all around the world.

   Each kind grows in only one part of the world.

4. How do humans destroy plants?

   Humans destroy the places where plants live.

   Humans make animal parks.

5. Why is it so important to save plants?

   Plants live longer than humans.

   Plants clothe us, feed us, and provide us with medicines.

5 Book 2.2/Unit 3
   The World's Plants Are in Danger

At Home: Have children name three favorite plants found where they live.

245

Choose a Reference Source

To find the information you need, you must sometimes look at more than one kind of **reference source**.

Look at the following four reference sources. Notice how each tells you something different.

Dictionary Entry

mall 1. a large enclosed shopping center 2. a large open space like a park (môl) noun, *plural* **malls**

Encyclopedia Entry

MALL. See SHOPPING CENTER

SHOPPING CENTER is a group of stores organized as a unit. The open area between them is usually called a mall. It may be covered and air conditioned. Some malls have restaurants, banks, hotels, medical care and theaters. Before World War II there were only ten malls in the U.S.

Nonfiction Book Title Page

THE MALL AS THE NEW TOWN:
Are Malls Taking Over America?

by Dominick Sandstrom

Telephone Directory Yellow Pages

Malls/Shopping Centers— Malls
Heritage Mall 555-9876
Highway 98 Mall 555-2389

Use the reference sources above to answer these questions. Write **True** or **False**.

1. The encyclopedia entry would give you an idea what's in a mall. _____

2. The nonfiction book includes a question as part of its title.

   _____

3. The dictionary entry gives the names and addresses of the local malls. _____

4. Under the entry "Malls/Shopping Centers," the telephone directory lists the phone numbers of all the separate stores in each mall. _____

At Home: Have children use several sources to investigate a subject that interests them. Then compare the different reference sources.

246

Book 2.2/Unit 3
The World's Plants Are in Danger   4

Main Idea

Read each story. Then read each main idea. Write two details from each story that support the main idea.

A traffic light tells you to stop and go. A flashing light warns of danger ahead. Holiday lights are red and green.

Main idea: A light can be a safety signal.

Detail: _____

Detail: _____

An ant has a pair of antennas on its head. Ants work hard to build their nests. Ants carry heavy loads of food to their nests.

Main idea: Ants are busy insects.

Detail: _____

Detail: _____

4 Book 2.2/Unit 3
The World's Plants Are in Danger

At Home: Ask children to draw a picture about one detail from each story.

247

Form Generalizations

Read the story. Then read the sentences below the story.
Write **Yes** next to each fact from the story. Write **No** if it is
not a fact from the story.

> I love summer weather in Texas. It is hot in June,
> and we go swimming. In July, the temperature may
> reach 100 degrees. We like to go barefoot in this kind of
> heat. In August, we start school. We wear shorts and
> cotton shirts to keep cool.

1. June is a hot month in Texas. _____

2. We can go swimming in June. _____

3. The weather is hot when we start school. _____

4. It is too cool to go barefoot in July. _____

5. It may be 100 degrees in October. _____

Read the sentences in the box. Write the generalization
and then write two details that support the generalization.

> Going barefoot is fun.
> Summers are hot in Texas.
> Shorts are good clothes for school.

Generalization: _____

Details: _____

_____

At Home: Have children write a generalization about
the weather during the past week in your city.

Figurative Language

Draw a line from each phrase to a saying that describes the underlined word.

1. The <u>road</u> turns and twists. The road is   as quick as a fox.

2. Jerry is a <u>fast</u> runner. He is   like a snake.

3. Our car is very <u>big</u>. It is   as big as a house.

4. That man is very <u>smart</u>. He is   as light as air.

5. The skater <u>glided</u> on the ice.   as mad as a hornet.
   She seemed

6. The bear became <u>angry</u>. He was   like a wise old owl.

7. The girl <u>hasn't eaten</u> all day.   as quiet as a mouse.
   She is

8. Sinbad makes very   as hungry as a wolf.

   <u>little noise</u>. He is

8 Book 2.2/Unit 3
The World's Plants Are in Danger

At Home: Have children choose three animals. Ask them to compare some characteristic of each to something else.

249

Multiple-Meaning Words

To figure out the meaning of a multiple-meaning word, you can see how it fits into the sentence.

The underlined words have more than one meaning. Fill in the circle next to the meaning of the underlined word.

1. The day was clear and without a cloud.

   ⓐ bright and sunny, without clouds

   ⓑ easy to understand

2. The directions were clear and easy to follow.

   ⓐ bright and sunny, without clouds

   ⓑ easy to understand

3. Time flies quickly when you are having fun.

   ⓐ to check the speed of

   ⓑ the passing of hours, days, and years

4. Can you time me while I run around the track?

   ⓐ to check the speed of

   ⓑ the passing of hours, days, and years

5. The workers will take a break for lunch.

   ⓐ to split into parts

   ⓑ a short rest time

Unit 3 Vocabulary Review

A. Find a word that means almost the same thing. Write the matching word on the line.

_____ 1. swift   always

_____ 2. save   fast

_____ 3. escaped   rescue

_____ 4. midnight   wild

_____ 5. forever   twelve A.M.

_____ 6. fierce   ran off

B. Use the words in the box to complete the questions. Write the words on the lines.

hidden	restaurant	wipe	audience

1. When the play ended, what did the _____ do?

2. Did you _____ up the milk you spilled?

3. Would you rather go to a _____ or eat at home?

4. Where is the gift _____?

10 Book 2.2/Unit 3
Unit 3 Vocabulary Review

At Home: Have children make up questions and answers for some of the words in Exercise A.

251

Unit 3 Vocabulary Review

A. Write a word from the box next to the word that means the opposite.

cheered	evenings	crowded	disappear

1. booed _____

2. empty _____

3. show up _____

4. mornings _____

B. Using the code below, write a word from the box next to the code.

accidents	desert	shoulder	cousins	golden	princess

a	b	c	d	e	f	g	h	i	j	k	l	m	n	o	p	q	r	s	t	u	v	w	x	y	z
!	@	#	$	%	^	&	*	(	)	_	~	=	+	{	[	}	]	|	\	>	.	,	'	?	<

1. !##($%+\| _____

2. $%\|%]\ _____

3. &{~$%+ _____

4. [](+#%\|\| _____

5. \|*{>~$%] _____

6. #{>\|(+\| _____

252
At Home: Have children write two of the words from Exercise A in code.

Book 2.2/Unit 3
Unit 3 Vocabulary Review
10